The Gh
of
PLYMOUTH

Nancy Hammonds

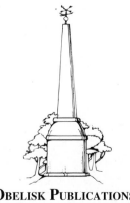

OBELISK PUBLICATIONS

ALSO IN THIS SERIES

The Ghosts of Exeter, *Sally and Chips Barber*
The Ghosts of Torbay, *Deryck Seymour*
The Ghosts of Berry Pomeroy Castle, *Deryck Seymour*
The Ghosts of Brixham, *Graham Wyley*
The Ghosts of Totnes, *Bob Mann*
Haunted Pubs in Devon, *Sally and Chips Barber*
Dark & Dastardly Dartmoor, *Sally and Chips Barber*
Ghastly and Ghostly Devon, *Sally and Chips Barber*
Murders and Mysteries in Devon, *Ann James*

OTHER TITLES OF INTEREST

The Great Little Plymouth Book, *Chips Barber*
Plymouth in Colour, *Chips Barber*
Around & About the Haldon Hills, *Chips Barber*
Diary of a Dartmoor Walker, *Chips Barber*
Diary of a Devonshire Walker, *Chips Barber*
The Great Little Dartmoor Book, *Chips Barber*
TV Programmes and Films Made in Devon, *Chips Barber*
Burgh Island and Bigbury Bay, *Chips Barber*
Weird and Wonderful Dartmoor, *Sally and Chips Barber*
Ten Family Walks on Dartmoor, *Sally and Chips Barber*
Six Short Pub Walks on Dartmoor, *Sally and Chips Barber*
The South Hams, *Chips Barber*
Beautiful Dartmoor, *Chips Barber*
Around & About Salcombe, *Chips Barber*
From the Dart to the Start, *Chips Barber*
Dartmouth and Kingswear, *Chips Barber*
Cranmere Pool – the First Dartmoor Letterbox, *Chips Barber*

We have over 130 Devon titles, for full list please send SAE to
Obelisk Publications, 2 Church Hill, Pinhoe, Exeter EX4 9ER

Plate Acknowledgements

Chips Barber for pictures on pages 3, 5, 12, 14, 16, 20, 24, 29 (top)
Western Evening Herald for picture on page 29 (bottom)
The Conservative Party for picture of Baroness Joan Vickers on page 10
Jane Reynolds for drawing on page 6 and cover picture

First published in 1996 by
Obelisk Publications, 2 Church Hill, Pinhoe, Exeter, Devon
Designed and Typeset by Sally Barber
Printed in Great Britain by
The Devonshire Press Ltd, Torquay, Devon

Introduction

Richly historic and atmospheric, Devon harbours a wealth of legend, folklore and weird tales. West Country folklore abounds with stories of strange happenings, no doubt embroidered with each retelling.

Plymouth is steeped in history. Sir Francis Drake's circumnavigation of the world, the voyage of the Pilgrim Fathers and James Cooke's explorations, all started here. Until Elizabethan times, there used to be two giant figures – Gog and Magog – carved in the turf on the Hoe – that great limestone ridge separating the harbour from the city centre, whose vast lawn is now broken up by war memorials. Also here, Francis Drake was said to be playing bowls when the Spanish Armada was spotted in 1588.

Many battles were fought here. During the Civil War Plymouth was staunchly Parliamentarian and successfully kept its port from the Royalists. When the monarchy was restored, Charles II had the imposing granite Royal Citadel built on the east side of the Hoe, guns pointed at the town as well as out to sea – so Plymothians were constantly reminded of who was the boss, and to show the lack of royal trust in the town and its people. Today the Citadel is home to the 29 Commando Regiment Royal Artillery.

From the Citadel battlements can be seen Sutton Harbour – where the English fleet assembled before tackling the Armada – and the Barbican, a tiny Saxon village whose harbour and fishing trade expanded during the Middle Ages. Many fine houses, built by Elizabethan merchants, still stand along mediæval cobbled streets, which escaped the German bombs that almost completely flattened Plymouth during the Second World War. The mixture of Tudor houses, timber-framed shops and pubs, and converted warehouses makes the Barbican interesting to explore – like the historic Elizabethan House on New Street, with a pole staircase made from a ship's mast, or the old monastery on Southside Street that ended up as the Black Friars Distillery.

Strategically-sited, Plymouth successfully recovered and was rebuilt into a vast shoppers' paradise while several stone tablets commemorate the colonisation of Virginia in 1584, the homecoming of the Tolpuddle Martyrs in 1838, and the landing of the first transatlantic flight in 1919, with pride of place going to the Pilgrim Fathers – whose one small step from the Barbican became a huge leap for America.

And with so much history, there are also fascinating tales of mystery, haunted houses and ghosts... naturally in old costume, mainly Tudor, Victorian or wartime. With VE and VJ Day 50th anniversary celebrations, stories of Blitz-time paranormal phenomena surfaced. Clearly Plymouth has a vast and active phantom population – and a treasure trove of recorded spooky phenomena!

It is not always older houses that are spooked; real ghosts seldom have a legend attached; and not everyone can encounter spectres. One family may spend a peaceful time in a house, while the next occupants experience odd happenings. Sometimes the city's housing officers are understandably cynical when tenants suddenly report hauntings and insist on being rehoused, yet at other times, they show real compassion and understanding towards a distressed family.

When BBC listeners were invited to tell spooky tales, many responded with some of Devon's most romantic ghost stories, with mostly 'episodic' English ghosts following conventional patterns. However, the West Country psychic researcher, the late Theo Brown believed, with ghost stories, "the more detailed the supposed history, the less likely it is to be genuine." She said, "Obviously any place where people have been at any time in history – or before – may have left an impression that may be manifested as a haunting. It is simply a matter of discovering the circumstances that will trigger off phenomena. Possibly lighting and weather conditions have a lot to do with it. In many cases we seem to be eavesdropping on a past scene; similar conditions would make this easier, just as certain moments in spring and autumn suddenly bring back our own memories so vividly."

This collection of tales about Plymouth's phantoms was gleaned from modern flats and council houses, as well as older and grander buildings, some no longer in the city – like Widey Court or Chubb's Hotel on Spooner's Corner. Many Plymothians seem quite happy to live with spectral housemates and will quite cheerfully discuss their ghostly encounters. A Plymouth estate agent swears he's had home-buyers actually asking for a resident ghost in a character property. But mention publicity and that's something else, a delicate problem, because they fear ridicule. However, many haunting cases have brought both psychics and clergymen readily stepping in to help coax the unfriendly ghost away – if prayers and blessings won't work, they may even resort to that taboo word... exorcism!

I have also included a few amusing incidents of 'ghosts' that never were – without ruining a good story! (I hope.)

Elizabethan Echoes

An archæologist with the Plymouth Museum experienced the fright of his life when he entered the Elizabethan House on New Street one October evening to prepare for a lecture.

Win Scutt, the museum's assistant keeper of archæology, had gone to the listed Tudor building on the Barbican on a Monday night in October 1983, to set the scene for a Workers Educational Association course. He and a colleague had been trying to tell the history of Plymouth through its folk songs. This intriguing practice evolved into an adult education programme, and he was planning to take people around the house to add a bit more atmosphere for their lectures. So he arrived a little earlier to make sure everything was in order.

It was dusk when Mr Scutt entered the building and went upstairs. He heard a noise and when he went into a room to investigate, he saw a cradle rocking inside... all by itself!

The experience so unnerved him that he rushed downstairs. The look of sheet-white horror was stamped on his face. He blurted out his ghostly encounter to the attendant downstairs. "But the attendant looked very sceptical when I told him," he recalled later.

By now some people were beginning to arrive for their course and Mr Scutt, unable to convince the attendant that he was neither seeing things nor playing a prank, enlisted the help of his adult students. "A couple of people on the course turned up and we went upstairs together – and the same thing happened!" he said. "It also took place a third time when I went back with some others."

Ever since the incident, neither Mr Scutt nor his solicited eye-witnesses would consider going back into the Elizabethan House by themselves. He said, "I have been trained to be a logical thinker, but I am at a loss to explain this."

Mr Scutt investigated more deeply into the circumstances surrounding the house and revealed, "I have since heard there have been other strange goings on in the house. Local cats that congregate in the courtyard will never dare go in the house and a cupboard drawer keeps on opening by itself." He added soberly, "I now know how frustrating it must be for people who see ghosts but have no witnesses. It's been quite a conversation piece in the office."

The Hampson Haunting

A modern ghost story that hit the local headlines involved a Plymouth naval wife who became so distressed by an unpleasant apparition in her flat that the Royal Navy flew her husband home on compassionate leave when it was feared she might have a mental breakdown. The Admiralty from Malta never admitted, of course, that they flew Leading Seaman William Hampson back to Plymouth because of a ghost allegedly causing havoc at his home in Stoke.

His wife, Dorothy, claimed she had seen the ghost – she called it 'he' – and it had thumped some of her young children in the back. Only a week after Bill's return in August 1955, it had manifested in their flat as a headless phantom, crouching behind a chair.

Bill, then 28, had left home in May, on HMS *Eagle*, but he said the disturbances began before his departure. At that time, he had merely shrugged it off and paid little heed to his wife's consternation. Something so formless and ethereal couldn't possibly endanger his family, he thought. However, after receiving his wife's increasingly frantic letters about being touched by the ghost, he decided to get home as quickly as possible to try to resolve the situation.

When he first reported the disturbances to his divisional officer, Bill asked him if he believed in ghosts. Not surprisingly, the officer replied, "no," and became a little sceptical.

There were four rooms in the house in Stoke, and in October 1954, the Hampsons took over its two upstairs ones, converted into a self-contained flat. Almost from the beginning, Dorothy Hampson, who was 29 at the time, felt it was eerie entering the inner intercommunicating room. "I felt there was something unseen but very real there," she recalled. "My husband, as men do, made little of it, and I myself thought I was imagining things. When, however, he returned to his ship and I was left in the house alone, I became convinced that there was more in it than met the eye.

"One day I was alone with the children when I felt a hand on my shoulder and a tug on the skirt of my dress. I told my husband of the incident and he tried to get compassionate leave, but it was not granted. When he went to sea, a woman friend stayed with me for a time. I told her nothing of what I had experienced. She had a newly-born baby, and one night she woke up in terror saying that someone had placed his hand on her shoulder and pulled at her nightdress. I was convinced then that my fears were founded."

Two other friends, a married couple, visited Dorothy and stayed with her – they heard a voice calling, "Betty, Betty." The couple decided to leave the house soon afterwards. "Who Betty is, I have not the faintest idea," said Dorothy. "As the two rooms below had become vacant, I moved into them and closed the door of the upstairs room." But despite sealing off the top rooms, the spectre continued to place a hand on her shoulder and tug Dorothy's dress. "Even the cat would burst into the room, with its fur bristling, snarling and spitting as if it had been frightened out of its life."

One day, she was horrified to learn something unseen had 'punched' her five-year-old son, Tony, in the back when he was in the bedroom alone. Little Tony was also puzzled as he told his mother someone had said "hello" to him, but when he turned, he saw nobody there.

6

Her ten-year-old daughter, Dorothy Ann, had a similar experience a couple of days later. The effect had been to make her extremely nervous and phobic about the ghost.

Her two-year-old child Jacqueline was chasing the cat one day, when her mother found her trembling and terrified on the landing. A fourth young child was in the North, being looked after by relatives.

The Hampsons were told that a priest had committed suicide there 40 years ago – "but whether it is true or not we do not know," said Bill. A spiritualist living nearby told them there was "an evil presence" in the house and had tried to contact the spirit to make it gradually go away. But it didn't.

By this time, Dorothy was so nervous that on one particularly stormy night in May 1954, she called on a family friend, Mr F. R. Jury, a city council member and a sidesman at St Michael's Church in Stoke. He tried to placate her and later discussed her plight with his vicar, the Reverend Maurice Heath, who contacted the Rural Dean, the Reverend J. W. G. Molland. Mr Molland, also vicar of St Gabriel's Church, asked Father N. H. Hanson, the assistant curate at St Peter's Church, to investigate and if necessary, lay to rest the unquiet spirit.

Father Hanson called at the Stoke house on a Friday in June and, although he himself encountered nothing supernatural, he took a serious view of the case and decided to bless the house that weekend. He accepted there could well be something in what Dorothy Hampson related. "These things do happen," he said. "They have happened elsewhere and I see no reason why they should not happen here. Supernatural occurrences are by no means impossible."

Father Hanson had interviewed Dorothy's woman friend and the couple who stayed at the flat – they were all equally emphatic that something unusual was happening. For a while after the house blessing, nothing was heard of the ghost, but close observation was kept to see if there was any recurrence – "If there is," said Mr Molland, "we shall probably hold a service of exorcism."

Mr Molland made no secret of his views of the hauntings. He said, "Candidly, I think there is something in it, but that is as far as I am prepared to go. I am not taking it seriously until there is further evidence. If it is substantiated, we shall act."

There was a strange emblem in the house, fixed to an upstairs door. It was a medallion, shaped like an Iron Cross, except with rounded edges. In a circle in the centre was a head and shoulders of what appeared to be Christ. Round the circle were the words, 'Love, Honour, Reparation' and over the head were the letters 'I H S' surmounted by a heart. Father Hanson speculated that it was an object of devotion placed there by a previous tenant. When Dorothy asked if the emblem could be removed, Father Hanson advised against it.

After blessing the house, there was some respite from the chilling manifestations, and Dorothy enjoyed her first full night's rest in weeks. If the ghost did walk that weekend, she did not hear it. Peace reigned – alas too briefly… then the haunting returned with a vengeance.

By this time, the press heard about the haunting and picked up rumours that Mr Molland might hold a service of 'exorcism.' They descended on the Stoke flat for more news.

Interviewed by *Western Morning News* and *Evening Herald* reporters, Dorothy disclosed that she had lost a stone in weight since the visitations started – her clothes showed this – but insisted she had never requested exorcism – "The house has been blessed," she said, "and after that I had every confidence I would be left in peace. But after a few days, it returned."

She said she had heard the ghost the previous evening – for about two minutes during the night, as it walked across the floor above. She revealed her feeling that anyone who thought they could rid her of the ghost was welcome to try, but she could now never rest in the house.

This brought a rash of visitors, and more reporters. Besides the local vicar, there was a man who believed he could draw the ghost with two sticks and a woman who wanted to play classical music on the piano to calm the spirit – but Dorothy declined the sticky offer and told the woman she had not got a piano. One Friday night, a visitor reported feeling aware of the ghostly presence and seeing a door close on its own. Five boys on school holiday called at the flat and asked to be allowed to sleep in two sealed-off haunted rooms. Dorothy told them it was impossible, as she would be held responsible if anything happened to them – "They wanted to write an essay about their experiences," she said.

Grilled by sceptical journalists, Dorothy said, "I am not imaginative – at least not more than the average person. The only other time I have considered supernatural happenings was when I was quite a young girl in Cheshire. I heard about a poltergeist in Runcorn. I was interested and heard first-hand accounts of how it behaved. This is just something I heard about and which interested me. I do not go around looking for ghosts."

Dorothy had never tried throwing anything at the spectral pest. She said, "I have been told never to anger a ghost. Sometimes when I feel the presence of something supernatural, I ask the ghost to go away." She said the 'presence' was usually accompanied by a strong perfumed smell and it played tricks with the house temperature – "It might suddenly go cold on a hot day, or perhaps during a cool night the temperature would shoot up."

Representatives of an American TV company contacted her for an interview, but Dorothy said, "I wasn't enthusiastic about TV. The idea of appearing on it didn't appeal to me."

Acting on advice, Dorothy decided to go away from the house with her children for a 10-day 'holiday' – with plans to find a more peaceful family home when she returned.

Meanwhile, back at Malta, the press reports managed to convince Bill's sceptical supervisor that he wasn't pulling a fast one – there was something genuinely distressing haunting his family. So the Navy granted Leading Seaman William Hampson compassionate leave in August and flew him home from Malta, because of his wife's health, retaining him in the Royal Naval Barracks at Devonport until his ship returned to Scotland the next month, and he could join it again in mid-September.

Unfortunately, Dorothy had no luck in her search for private accommodation. She told reporters, "During all this trouble, I have followed up nearly every advertisement for unfurnished accommodation, but I have been unlucky every time. When I say I have three children, the landladies turn me down."

She was advised to contact the housing department of the local corporation for help, but the chairman of Plymouth City Council's Housing Committee in 1955, W. A. Miller, said if Mrs Hampson applied for a council house, her request would be treated in the usual way "through the normal channels." There was a special committee to deal with applications where circumstances were abnormal, but he said there was no question of preferential treatment – Mrs Dorothy Hampson would have to take her turn.

Bill's home leave, albeit short, was a timely consolation and delighted her – "I feel I just cannot face up to things when Bill is away, and I am glad that he is here with me, now that I have returned from my 10-day holiday," she said. "I am naturally glad to have my husband home, but I haven't reduced myself to this state of nerves merely to get him home. I like being a sailor's wife. I agreed to his joining the Navy and to live the life he wants." She pointed out, "Yes, I would like a council house, but then, I would any home."

Knowing how terrified his wife was and how desperately she was trying to find another place to live, Bill wasted no time writing to Plymouth's housing manager for an interview, pointing out the urgency of their situation. They were already on the housing list.

A house said to be troubled by a ghost was the subject of a question put by Mr K. J. Adams to the chairman of Plymouth City Council's Housing Committee, Mr W. A. Miller, at their meeting on 5 September, 1955, it was reported.

Mr Adams was told if there was a case for rehousing the family living there, the Tenancies Sub-committee would consider the case on its merits. It would not authorise the allocation of a tenancy to any applicant unless satisfied that it was the proper course to adopt.

Time was running out; Bill was due to rejoin his ship on 15 September, and still no new home was yet available – "My husband has written to the Corporation housing manager, but has not been able to get an appointment," she anxiously told the reporter, who had become a sympathetic friend. Bill had also written to Miss Joan Vickers, their MP for Devonport, to seek her help to find another home. He too was finding it "rather suffocating in the rooms". He said, "There are strange noises, and not only at night. Even in the daylight, I am prepared to swear that someone walks across the ceiling above quite heavily. It is liable to happen at any time. My wife would not sleep with the light off and had a fixation that this thing could be dangerous in the dark, especially with the children."

Then came the nastiest experience of all that brought the greatest detrimental effect and sheer terror to Dorothy.

After a relatively peaceful night, Dorothy had a spiritualist friend, who was visiting them socially, when she suddenly went into a trance while they were talking about the recent disturbances. Her husband and a few friends were present with her at the time when the spiritualist contacted the spectre.

Bill recalled Dorothy was sitting in the dining room with him and the spiritualist friend, when suddenly she turned round and screamed in horror. She saw a black and white phantom, without head and shoulders, crouching behind her friend.

"There was a big explosion right behind this French chair where I am sitting," said Dorothy. "He stood with his arms folded, and I was scared to death."

Letters of comfort and sympathy flowed in from well-wishers, some offering advice to the Hampsons. A writer from Oklahoma advised, "I suggest that you employ a university-trained doctor of psychology and a well-trained detective, and check on all known enemies your wife may have." Another American wrote, "There is something buried in the house and the ghost is trying to contact you because it wants you to have it."

However they did not ease the one worry preying on Dorothy's mind – "No one has yet written offering us somewhere to live," she said. "I am determined for the sake of the three children and my own health, to find another home. Anywhere will do."

She was determined not to stay on in her haunted Stoke flat and was determined to move when her husband rejoined his ship – "I will not stay here with the children, even if I have to walk the streets all night," she told her reporter friend.

Meanwhile Devonport MP Joan Vickers dropped in, after the Hampsons' invitation,

Joan Vickers

and declared to reporters, "I believe in ghosts. In fact I've seen them on two occasions." Miss Vickers promised, "I will write to the Corporation asking what are your chances of a council house." She pointed out though that it was a matter entirely for the local council. Even so, her visit took a tremendous weight off Dorothy's mind. Her reaction was, "It is a relief to find someone who doesn't think I'm imagining things."

Eventually, it was Bill's employers, the Royal Navy, who stepped in a second time to save the day. The naval machinery worked swiftly again and managed to find the Hampsons a partially-furnished flat in the North Road district – with enough time for them to be moved out of their haunted flat the very weekend before Bill's shore leave ended. A contented Dorothy and her family moved into their new home on a Tuesday, as soon as formalities were settled – two days before Bill had to return to his ship.

"I feel much happier now," Dorothy told a *Western Morning News* reporter in September, 1955.

Terror on Brake Farm

What happened in a Plymouth council bungalow on Brake Farm one night that left a grandmother and her teenaged grandson quaking with fear, defied explanation. A neighbour heard the rumpus and witnessed the devastation when he went to investigate, and a parish priest also believed that something happened in the home of Mrs Val Leech which terrified her and her 15-year-old grandson, Quentin Hoskins, almost out of their wits. They were convinced a poltergeist had wreaked havoc inside their home.

Widow Mrs Leech, aged 64, loved her one-bedroomed bungalow, in which she had lived for eight years since her husband died in 1982, and she remained determined to stay on there despite what happened, ghost or otherwise.

It all took place one Thursday night, when she and Quentin were just dropping off to sleep. The noises began… and during the next six hours, the walls were thumped, and chairs, pictures, books and ornaments were hurled all around the room. She had a wall-hanging which housed a phial containing holy water – this was smashed. As the terror escalated, Mrs Leech had to hang on to her grandson. It appeared as if unseen hands had grabbed the boy's ankles and were dragging him towards the bedroom door. And the bedroom door was opened and slammed shut with such force that its veneer panelling on both sides was ripped upwards. A chair that they placed to keep the door open was found to have been crushed. The duvets on both their beds in the room were repeatedly dragged off towards the bedroom door more than ten times.

"I am a devout Catholic but I am not a religious maniac," said Mrs Leech. "Also I am not easily frightened. Thank goodness my grandson was here – and my neighbour came round in the middle of the night to find out what the noise was all about. Otherwise people would say I was a silly old woman who was losing her mind."

Quentin, a schoolboy, said, "I thought the night would never end." He felt from their

The Ghosts of Plymouth

experience of the destructive manifestation that "there was anger there – the things thrown about missed us by inches," he said.

Their neighbour, Harry Chapman, had been asleep in his chair next door when he was awakened around midnight by the sound of things being heavily thumped about. He said, "I came round to ask Val what the heck was going on. When I went in the loud banging stopped, but I could see the phial of holy water had been smashed, and Val and Quentin were obviously scared to death."

After he left, the mayhem began happening again until, finally, at around 4.45 a.m. on Friday, their ordeal ended.

When they were told about the terrifying happenings, Mrs Leech's family were very concerned and contacted the parish priest. Father Dennis Collen, of St Peter's Church, visited the house. After listening to what had happened, he said, "I have heard of such cases before. In fact I heard of one in the home of a parish priest. Sometimes it can be a distressed soul who is calling for our prayers."

The Roman Catholic priest led the family in prayers at Mrs Leech's home and sprinkled holy water around and blessed the bungalow. Fortunately this time, the church seemed to have helped to resolve their predicament, or perhaps the spirit decided to manifest itself less violently… for nothing more was heard from the bungalow down on Brake Farm.

Ghost stars on camera

One Plymouth pensioner had actually taken a picture which he claimed had shown a ghost in his Union Street flat at Edgcumbe House. The man, Jim Whiteley, who was then 63, reportedly captured the spectre on film on a Saturday night in August, 1989.

Mr Whiteley had been taking photographs of the nightlife in the Union Street club land area from his window. His flat overlooked the street. It was when he put his camera down, and had just sat down to watch a programme on television that a shimmering light suddenly appeared in a corner of the room. This, he said, gradually evolved into the face of a woman.

Jim Whiteley grabbed his camera and snapped away frantically. His pictures showed what appeared to be a face, surrounded by a halo of light. He was convinced it was a ghost and not the reflection from the neon lights of the clubs and bars outside.

The *Evening Herald* published one of Jim Whiteley's photographs showing the hint of a face – white blobs on black background, but this could be more conclusive. "It was not a reflection from outside," he insisted. "I've tried every night since to see if she'll appear again, but she hasn't. She was there for only a few minutes, then disappeared altogether."

Mr Whiteley said he believed in the existence of ghosts. He told a reporter from the *Evening Herald* that he had once before seen a ghost while working in a Liverpool biscuit factory – "It used to play havoc with our gear," he said.

Some of Plymouth's show business establishments also boast of their own ghost stars. Westward TV and later Television South West, or TSW, once had their studios at Derry's Cross – not far from Derry's Clocktower, which was named after a former Mayor of Plymouth, William Derry.

Radio presenter George Pridmore, during his programme, "Devon's Week" – 'This week thirty years ago' – broadcast by Radio Devon in June, 1994, said it was believed that these television studios had been built on the site of a graveyard where French prisoners-of-war were buried.

The truth is still out there…

Many people who had worked in the studio buildings were convinced there was something weird present, with all sorts of ghostly goings-on in the building. The night watchmen at TSW believed they heard voices in the night. "In a place where you could have heard a pin drop in the wee small hours, these nocturnal noises often punctuated the stony silence, and when the voices could be clearly heard, the people who heard them were convinced they spoke fluently in French," said George Pridmore's radio broadcast.

It is said that one of the movie houses, also at Derry's Cross, was haunted by a ghost named Emma. She was possibly an actress from the old Theatre Royal before it was demolished in 1937. Or she could have been one of the permanent residents of the nearby Westwell Cemetery, which has since been built over.

Mary Ann Penrose, of Stonehouse, tells of the old Palace Theatre down Union Street, that, around the turn of the century, used to be owned by a family known as 'the fashionable Hoyles.' She said Mrs Hoyle was supposed to have been a tragic lady – and it was rumoured that she still haunted the theatre she once owned. Ms Penrose pointed out that the Palace Theatre was probably the most ornate surviving Victorian building in Plymouth.

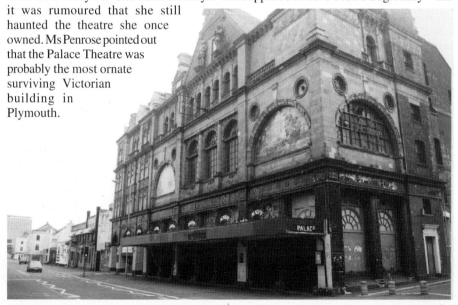

The actress and the ghosts

One of the best-known hauntings, widely reported in Plymouth's showbiz circles at the time – and well documented by the Devonshire Association – was encountered by a Georgian actress, Mrs Hunn, who had pursued her acting career, working in the provinces, after her third marriage.

Mrs Hunn was the mother of the British Prime Minister, George Canning, who was born in 1770, and died in 1827 while still in office at Number 10 Downing Street.

When Mrs Hunn first arrived in Plymouth one day, to take up an acting engagement at the Plymouth Theatre, her stage colleague, John Bernard, recommended some lodgings which were offered at a very low rent because of a weird snag – the house, which belonged to a carpenter, had the reputation of being haunted. The actress cheerfully accepted this, saying it would not be the first time she had had to do with a ghost – and she settled in peacefully with her maid and children.

After dark there was little to do in those days, so on her first night there, after sending her children off to bed, she lit two candles and read a book for about half an hour. Her bedroom was immediately above the carpenter's workshop. All was quiet for a while, then she became conscious of a terrible noise originating from below – as if there were several men at work downstairs, knocking, hammering, sawing and planing wood and engaged in generally noisy activity at a time when there should be no one in the workshop.

Being a woman of considerable courage, Mrs Hunn resolved to investigate this mystery herself. So, she took off her shoes, in order to tread softly so that if there were any unauthorised people downstairs, they would not hear her approach. Then, with her candle in her hand, she very carefully opened the door to the workshop. Instantly silence fell – all was still, not a mouse was stirring. She saw that the tools and the wood, and everything else, were lying as they had been left by the workmen when they went away. Mrs Hunn walked around the workshop and examined every part of the place, until she was satisfied that there was no one there, and that nobody could get into it. Then she went back upstairs to her room. She was just beginning to doubt her own senses, and to question whether she had really heard the noise or merely imagined it all, when the noise returned and continued without interruption for half an hour.

However, she decided to ignore the incident and went to bed. The next day she told no one of what took place that night. She decided to watch another night to see if the incident recurred before mentioning the supernatural happening to anyone. This strange scene was acted over again the second night, and again she was unable to discover the cause of it.

So, the next day, at the theatre, she mentioned her experiences to her friend, John Bernard, and to the owner of the house. Mr Bernard was quite prepared to believe her but her landlord, the carpenter, was highly sceptical, despite the fact that his earlier tenants had also complained of strange goings-on. However, he agreed to stand watch at his house with her that night. The noise began as before, but the carpenter was so horror-struck that, instead of entering his workshop as Mrs Hunn had wished him to do, he rushed straight out into the street. However, cowardly though he might have been, the carpenter proved to be a decent man – he let Mrs Hunn and her family continue staying in the house that whole summer rent-free.

The phantom workmen continued their nightly routine, but as they appeared harmless enough, Mrs Hunn and her household chose to ignore them. When referring afterwards to the supernatural adventure, she observed, as their use of her temporary home became second nature, and their activity predictable, she grew indifferent to their presence and even felt some relief when the anticipated nocturnal noises came – she said she felt sure that if on any night the ghostly carpenters had not pursued their visionary labours, she might have been quite frightened, in case they should pay her a visit upstairs!

John Bernard recorded Mrs Hunn's ghost story in his book, *Retrospections of the Stage*. From this, another writer, Mrs Catherine Crowe, took it for her early Victorian collection of ghost stories, *Night Side of Nature*, published between 1848 and 1855.

The ghost of Ward 13

One can expect hospitals – being places where life and death hang in the balance – to harbour ghost stories, and being among Plymouth's most active hospitals until Derriford Hospital took over their duties recently, it comes as no surprise that Freedom Fields Hospital, and Greenbank Hospital across the road from it, have their share of phantoms.

At least ten nurses in Ward 13 – the geriatric ward of Plymouth's Freedom Fields Hospital – had reportedly been at the receiving end of a pesky poltergeist. This restless spirit was said to have been switching lights on and off, slamming the door, throwing drugs on the floor and even tapping staff on the shoulder. Some nurses had asked for an exorcist to evict the surgical spirit. However, their request was denied by the Plymouth Health Authority.

Freedom Fields' then assistant district general hospital manager, Philip Sanders, explained, "There is no question of calling in an exorcist. Staff have said that whatever it is does not appear to be nasty, so they are not unduly worried."

Meanwhile, the activities of this troublesome ghost reached the *Evening Herald* and a reporter was sent there to investigate in April 1989. However, as is usually the case with supernatural phenomena – they seem to be shy of journalists – the ghost of Ward 13 at Freedom Fields Hospital went temporarily into hiding.

"No one has reported any further instances in the last week anyway," said Mr Sanders.

Normal hauntings resumed eventually, and some nurses still claim there is more to the creaks and groans within the now nearly unoccupied buildings, than can be blamed on the wind and old timbers.

The old Royal Albert Hospital at Devonport – whose buildings used to start at the northern end of Marlborough Street before it was demolished in the early 1980s – also harboured a ghost – a female spirit. She was thought to have been a long-serving nurse there.

Washbourne Close and Wright Close have sprung up on the old Royal Albert site. This incorporated the old towers of the former medical premises as a residential estate of houses and flats for owner occupation. Some residents of the present homes have claimed to experience paranormal activity.

Phantoms in the rubble

The Blitz on Plymouth by German bombers during the Second World War was followed by a rash of supernatural stories that emerged from the rubble and left such a lasting impression on those who experienced them that many of these people could recall them today as vividly and with the same feelings of bewilderment as when they first had these ghost encounters about fifty years ago.

The lady vanishes...

In the wake of a particularly devastating air raid, a ten-year-old girl and her eight-year-old brother were walking among the ruins of the Octagon in Union Street, searching for their family cat. Quite suddenly, almost unnoticed, a lady had appeared at their side. She silently started to help them in their search. Then she appeared to stumble. When the children reached out for her hand to help her regain her balance, they found to their enormous surprise, she faded away into thin air! They looked around for her but they could not see any crater or trench in the ruins into which the lady could have fallen. The two frightened children later told their friends and family members, "She just vanished." They also realised afterwards that the lady had not said a single word to them.

Fatherly love

Another victim of the Blitz, a young lad who was lying ill, was surprised to see his father unexpectedly appear by his bedside, trying to console him.

The man did not speak, but his fatherly presence was very comforting to the boy, who felt soothed and was able to rest. His mother, who had been seriously injured during the bombing, was in hospital, leaving her sister to look after the boy. Her son was unaware at the time that his father and his younger brother had both been killed during an air raid the previous evening.

Later, when the boy woke up feeling better, and he told his aunt that his dad had been by his bedside, the boy's aunt at first thought the lad was hallucinating because of his illness. However, she soon realised that her nephew had actually seen the ghost of his late father by his bedside, caring for him at a time of great anguish and distress. It was the boy's aunt who recalled this supernatural miracle during the 50th anniversary of the end of the Second World War.

He died yesterday

There was another case of a dead person being sighted after a spate of German bombing. A woman saw an old man who was her neighbour in Kinterbury Street, Plymouth. When she told her friend later that she had just seen the old man, her friend was astonished – and she startled the woman by announcing that the neighbour she said she had seen alive and walking, had in fact been reported killed during an air raid the previous day.

A Plymouth writer, Ernest Pearn, who had been collecting ghost stories from the Second World War, said, "There were many reports of 'smells of decay' and of animal-like screams from different parts of the city, long after the Blitz. Other people reported feelings of deep depression and sorrow when standing on or near certain areas."

Phantom of the inferno

Several Plymouth firemen at different times had encountered one same apparition from the same building set ablaze during the wartime Blitz. This happened at Spooner's Corner at the junction of East Street and Old Town Street, on what used to be the site of the Chubb's Hotel during Victorian times. That was probably the first appearance of the frightening figure, probably that of a lady – but according to some of the firemen who

had seen the spectre, it was not too distinct. The ghost was always accompanied by a strange animal-like screeching when she appeared to rise from the blaze. Then she pointed to the flames and disappeared into them.

Although her unearthly screeching was heard in other parts of the blazing building, all the reported sightings of this spectre had always been at the hotel site. The animal noises were heard many times on that spot – long after the fires had been overcome. "Although at first the noises were really frightening, we got to like the old girl after a while," said one of the firemen who witnessed the apparition. "Several of our chaps saw it at different times and heard the screams which she made, many times after Spooner's had been burnt out."

Other firemen agreed that they had heard many other colleagues talking about it at the station long afterwards and thought it was a leg-pull, but they soon realised that the ghostly sightings and particularly the noise were being taken seriously by others in the station.

One senior fireman suggested that the 'animal-like' noises could have been made by the branch, which was the nozzle-head of the hoses, and which did emit a high-pitched screaming when under great pressure. This was offset by the fact that the noises had been heard long after the fire. It was also suggested that the apparition could have been a hallucination with a 'fire causation' or the result of extreme fatigue… but this does not explain the display on different occasions. The sightings had been verified by various firemen at different times.

One witness Oliver Lodge suggested, "Such ghosts could be a replay of a tragedy that had occurred in the same place as the apparition." However, there was no record of any such tragedy having happened in the hotel during Victorian times.

Serena Penrose of Stonehouse, Plymouth, also saw "a really strange sight" as the blaze took hold of one shop in Old Town Street during the March 1941 blitz on Plymouth. She and her sister, Mary Ann, thought "the flames took the shape of a person, with the face clearly visible for a sustained period, getting larger and larger until the ghost – for that is how it appeared to be – was towering about 40 feet in the air, as if it was feeding on the energy of the fire."

The flamboyant couple

On a cold winter's evening, a young soldier arrived back in Plymouth on leave and was walking home along Cobourg Street when he suddenly realised an air raid was in progress. The only person in sight in the deserted street was an air raid warden, who was calling out to him to take cover.

The soldier continued walking faster towards the warden, when he suddenly became aware of a young couple also walking, but more slowly, in front of him. Apart from their sudden appearance on the street, their unusual attire also commanded attention. It was winter time but, despite the chilly night, they were wearing quite flimsy summer clothes. The man wore a brilliant yellow and black blazer and white flannel trousers, and a straw boater on his head. His girlfriend was just as lightly dressed – in a thin dress – but the most striking feature about her was the enormous blue hat she wore. It was adorned with a large feather. The two of them were so absorbed with each other's company that they appeared oblivious to everything else happening around them.

When the soldier, hurrying on, had caught up with them and the warden, the couple seemed to vaporise into thin air – they completely disappeared! The warden seemed unaware of the apparition the young man had seen. The soldier soon reached his home in Salisbury Road, but before he could mention anything about his weird encounter, his sister greeted him and asked, "Who were the couple who came along the road outside with you?" Astonished, he protested that he had come home alone, but the sister persisted, "What about that blazer and the hideous blue feathered hat? Surely you must have seen them?" The soldier then told her the story of his first encounter with the unknown couple.

A few hours later, his other sister came home and said to both of them, "There was a young couple by the gate outside this house when I approached. They were dressed in the most gaudy summer dress and it is freezing outside... the man's blazer was yellow with black stripes, and that hat which the woman wore was blue, very large, with an equally large feather!" The soldier and his first sister rushed towards the window, but she called out to them, "You won't find them there now – they disappeared when I entered the gate!" Then she halted them both in their tracks with... "In fact I walked through them."

These were three sightings of the same apparition, at different places in Plymouth, at different times, by three different people, all of whom were completely unaware of each other's ghostly experience!

Another case of multiple sightings took place in a police training centre, where senior officers saw a nun playing snooker! Fifty years ago, a convent had stood on the site of the centre.

Dream time...

Dreams can sometimes turn out to be paranormal experiences, when they warn you of things to come, as in the case of one Royal Navy sailor during the war.

The Plymouth seaman was on shore leave and had just survived an air raid on the city. That night, in a dream, he saw his ship being torpedoed. Though it must have being slightly unnerving, he shrugged it off. Three days later, when he rejoined his ship, it was torpedoed off Dieppe – he turned out to be one of the few survivors!

Supernatural soirée

Broadcaster George Pridmore told of another strange phenomenon involving a seaman in his "Devon's Week", 'This week thirty years ago' spot, on Radio Devon in June 1994.

Before the war, an immigrant Irish family had moved into the cramped flat that was above a jeweller's shop in King Street – this used to run almost at a right angle into Western Approach before the German bombers wreaked havoc and razed many of its buildings to the ground. The family, probably Roman Catholic, was a large one with many children. Almost as soon as they had taken up residence, their ghostly troubles began – their children started seeing things that were most definitely ghosts of various types.

The supernatural activity was intense – with poltergeists weighing in with their own brand of mischief. The parents had to act swiftly so they summoned a priest. As there appears to be no further documentation of their unwanted guest, we can only assume that the priest's action was sufficient to quell what seemed to be a spiritual riot.

However, the property as a whole was quite large and possessed yet another ghost – this one seemed to operate independently of the previous ones. The latter spectre was a creature of habit, favouring the end of long summer evenings for his spiritual soirées. On such nights, he would make his visitations – members of the household were full of anticipation at his late evening appearances. They would lie in bed, almost knowing when his apparition would arrive, and there was no mistaking just what he was – a former seaman. He bore all the attributes of one who had lived a life on storm-tossed seas. He was the tall, silent type and when he stalked his way around the house, he would stare at its occupants, but he never spoke a word to them.

The only noises he emitted were the occasional murmurings, moaning and groaning that seemed to suggest that he was a ghost on a mission to find something. But what his quest was we shall never know, for the shop and the flats that were above it have gone… and so has the ghost.

Where have all old soldiers gone?
Old soldiers never die, they say, but neither do they always fade away…

A retired *Evening Herald* columnist, Douglas Selleck, who lives in Plymstock, recalled that while visiting a school a few years ago, he heard at least a dozen teenagers swear they had seen the ghost of a soldier in an old tunnel… Weston Mill Tip. Unlike usual ghostly phenomena which are mainly nocturnal, this apparition appeared during the school dinner hour – in broad daylight!

Douglas said, "There was no mistaking their frightened conviction, but of course there was an atmosphere of mutually induced hysteria. It caught on so that some of the boys – for whom neither policeman nor probation officer held any terrors – were telling stories of ghostly happenings in the local cemetery for weeks afterwards."

Dark tales of Devonport
Many strange other-worldly incidents appear to have happened in the Devonport area over the years and some of these tales of the disembodied become part of the local legends. However, apart from those that made it to the archives of the Devonshire Association or the Plymouth Institution, written records of them are hard to find.

Mutiny mystery
One story concerns Fletcher Christian, the man who led the mutineers of the *Bounty* in the Pacific. In 1789, Fletcher Christian and his men set Captain William Bligh, with his officers, adrift in a small boat with some supplies, and eventually ran the *Bounty* aground on the reef around the Pitcairn Islands. The mutineers settled there, where their descendants still live today. Returning to England would have seen them at the gallows.

Some 20 years after the mutiny, one of Captain Bligh's naval officers from the *Bounty* happened to be walking in Fore Street, Devonport, one night when a man who looked remarkably like Fletcher Christian passed him. He immediately turned and followed, calling Christian's name – but within a few yards, the man simply vanished! Miss Joan

M. Stivey, who recalled this weird story, asks, "Was it a flesh and blood man with a guilty conscience, ducking into a dark alley or doorway to avoid arrest? Would Fletcher Christian have returned to Devonport, risking life and freedom? Or was it an uneasy spirit seeking to find out if his victims had survived their ordeal? All we know is that an extensive search failed to find any trace of the man."

The Smiling Sailor

Ghostly footsteps, vacuum cleaners that mysteriously turned themselves off, and bearded apparitions humming uncanny tunes, revealed that the spirit of the 'Smiling Sailor' was on the march again at Devonport Royal Dockyard recently.

Even hardened naval officers had confessed themselves baffled after a series of reported hauntings in an 18th century building over about the last four months of 1987.

Cleaners refused to enter the Master Ropemaker's House in the South Yard – which in 1987 became the headquarters for the Navy's surveying operations – while lights had been left on all night to allay their fears and there had even been talk of an exorcism to rid the building of the uneasy spirit.

The *Western Morning News* in December, 1987, reported Lieutenant Commander Neil Scruton, who was based in those offices, as saying, "I am normally sceptical about ghosts but even I have an open mind on this one. There is definitely something going on." According to Lt Cdr Scruton, at least two cleaners, a leading Wren, and he himself, had experienced the ghostly presence. One cleaner who was by herself early one morning, heard footsteps in the room above. She went up and found nobody there. Returning to the kitchen, she experienced a sudden drop in temperature, turned round and saw "a big bearded chap humming a tune". He then disappeared.

Another cleaner had refused to work alone in the office after her vacuum cleaner was mysteriously turned off twice.

Dockyard historian Peter Ridolfo, curator of the dockyard museum said the hauntings were probably the work of the 'Smiling Sailor', who was hanged for murder in the late 18th century. "This effigy has been seen around the South Yard part of the base for many years," he said. "He always appears as a bearded man with a smile on his face."

'Beware nutter!'

Several supernatural sightings are reported to come from inside Devonport Dockyard. Miss Stivey, who has lived in the area all her life, knows some of the stories of "strangely dressed people seen around the old market place – men and women, who seem to be wearing old fashioned clothes." She said, "Sometimes they go around a corner, or else a second look as one gets closer, finds no one there."

One such phantom is a man seen near the Ropery. He is quite distinctive – he wears a wide belt and braces over his shirt, but no jacket. Miss Stivey, who lives in Stoke, tells this story of an encounter with the spectre, "Near the gazebo, a scruffy man, leering horribly was seen by three sailors returning to their ship at Number 1 Jetty. The two ahead called back to their mate, 'Beware nutter!' – at which the menacing figure vanished. It was assumed that they had supped beer over well, and the story told by all three of the young men was ignored. But a few nights later, more people saw an evil-looking man on the same road and reported it to the police, who carried out a search of the area – finding no one!"

Girl in the attic

The Rope Master's House is now a surgery, and Miss Stivey knows at least two different sources of stories about the surgery. Its attic is supposed to be empty, but noises can be heard from it, and this prompts people to investigate. Some have then found the figure of a young girl, about eight to ten years old, playing with a doll. Miss Stivey says, "In one instance, when the clinic housekeeper asked her name, the child disappeared. Another time, the little girl just smiled without answering, walking into the next room – but she was not there when the lady followed right at the child's heels."

She says local inquiries have unearthed the story of a little girl, who had died there – on the day her parents had moved into the house. "In the same building, lights have been found on in the middle of the night – with doors and windows firmly locked and the security patrols adamant that all was dark during earlier rounds," she says. "One lady was alone in a corridor there when hands were placed firmly against her shoulders and she was pushed strongly along the passage. And several people have reported seeing the figure of a man at the back attic window – when the house was empty."

The door handle turned...

There is a house in Pasley Street where one of Miss Stivey's friends once lived. She recalls one frightening time when she was standing in the passage talking to another lady – and the handle of the closed door beside them started to turn... but thankfully for them, it did not open – "Gradually the handle started to rattle and was soon turning and shaking violently," she said. "However, the door was not locked and the room was unoccupied.

There was no wind and nothing else moved or shook. The front door stood firm, pictures and the hall stand did not even quiver – and none of the people in the other houses around experienced any disturbance."

Joan Stivey had previously lived in Millbridge, and she points out, "The Millbridge area certainly had its share of ghosts. I personally

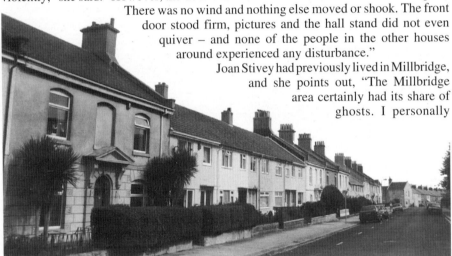

experienced several uncanny happenings," she says, "many were slight and of no dramatic value. For instance, while living alone in the house, a vague shadow caught the corner of my eye as I was engaged in the very humdrum job of washing up dirty dishes. As I looked, the curtain at the end of the passage moved slightly as a black skirt vanished. I was there in a second, switching on all the lights around, but there was nothing to be seen – all the windows still fastened and the doors locked, no wind, no explanation. Only a glimpse of a long, black skirt... such as my grandmother, long dead, had worn!"

On one occasion, there was an electrician working in her house. "Having an afternoon cuppa, we had him join us in the dining room," she says. "He was talking, then he broke off. After a pause, he said, 'Someone came in, I heard your door.' I replied that I'd check, but I knew I had put the small finger catch over the door – and I had! 'Strange,' said the electrician, 'I'm sure I heard your door open'."

Dog gone distress

Some years earlier, she recalls experiencing a much more scary incident. She says, "I went up to bed leaving my Dad watching television, in black and white in those days. It was winter and he was about 80 years old – so I lit the gas fire in his bedroom and firmly shut the door to keep the warmth in. Going to my room, I went through the normal routine of putting the next day's clothes ready, then brushing my hair and writing out the next day's shopping list. Then suddenly, from outside my door came very loud howls of a dog in fear or in distress. For a minute I froze, thinking, 'Boyso! What's happened?' But I remembered our dog, Boyso, had died 18 months ago. And then I heard the sound of slow heavy footsteps come up the stairs and Dad's door open. Still shaking, I forced myself to go downstairs to check that Dad was OK and if he had heard anything. I found the staircase in darkness… likewise Dad's room, which was empty, but the room door was wide open. I could hear muted sounds from the television, from downstairs. Was he ill? I wondered, and as I was the only one there to check, so down I went and, with a deep breath, opened the living room door. There my father looked around and said, 'Oh, I thought you'd gone to bed. I'm coming now'."

Maid for eternity

There were many times when Joan Stivey went out to "snatch a brief hour of a sunny Sunday afternoon", to sit in her back courtyard. And several times while relaxing there, she "heard the tinkle of cups and saucers being set out." She says, "I thought I was to be treated to a cup of tea I hadn't made myself. But never did Dad appear with that longed for cup. And when the next house became empty, and still I heard tea being laid, I at last realised that a mistress or maid of earlier years was still at work."

Bogeywoman in the basement

For her, the most convincing touch to a supernatural yarn were the occasions when other people also remarked on a strange happening. One day, a little four-year-old little friend of hers was visiting her grandmother, when she dropped her ball, which rolled down the basement stairs – and she asked the two women to fetch it for her. They told her, "No Pam, you pick it up."

"But no!" says Miss Stivey. "She would not go downstairs. Eventually she explained, 'I don't like that lady down there'. Of course we said all the usual things – that she was being silly, and no one was down there, et cetera. After tea, her grandmother Kay and I were looking at some old family photos when little Pam came along and picked up one snapshot. She said firmly, 'That's the lady who was downstairs'."

Dad's ghost waved back

Her father died in 1971 – and then there was another ghost to haunt the house. Joan Stivey explains, "Several months after my Dad died, I took my cat to the vet just up the road. His wife was also his assistant and they had known us many years. While in the surgery, she asked after my father. My reply was that my father had died. Obviously that left her shaken. She told me, 'But when I saw him at your window this week, I waved to him as I drove by – I always do. He was sitting by the side window, looking down the street – and he waved back.' I shook my head and said the only thing I could. 'Sorry, my dear,' I told her, 'but my father died last December'."

Flying saucer eyes

In 'Dock', Devonport, in 1810, no woman or child would venture out after dark, for fear of a night-roaming ghost with 'saucer eyes'. It was said to have been the eyes of a recently deceased waterman. His attractive widow had quickly found consolation with a local baker. According to locals, this caused 'the oven fire to burn blue with revenge', and the spectre that materialised apparently uttered shrieks, threw tins around, and made the bread heavy and inedible. The apparition hovered over the house until the early hours, then floated off across the fields to Stoke Church, leaving a suffocating atmosphere behind it. This sounds more like a chimney fire than anything else.

The poltergeist of Charlotte Street

One of the best-documented paranormal phenomena around the Devonport area involved a house of more than a hundred years old, that used to stand in Charlotte Street. This was haunted by a most mischievous poltergeist, and its numerous highly dramatic manifestations had baffled everyone who encountered them, including the local police and the City Engineer's Department. This highly active spirit made its presence felt in a most physical manner and there were many reports of its antics from several different reliable witnesses.

The spook reportedly rattled some curtain poles – and also threw some extremely heavy curtain poles downstairs. There was a wardrobe in a room that kept falling across a bed. The floor was checked and found to be quite level – so this could not be blamed for the wardrobe tipping. An oil-lamp detached itself from a wall and was dashed up the stairs. One woman said, "It had great fun with a pail of water which was kept on the landing – first it moved the pail across the landing to the head of the staircase, then, keeping the pail roughly upright, it bumped it down twelve steps, sloshing a fair amount of water on the staircase as it did so."

A flat-iron mysteriously jumped off a stove downstairs, and was seen flying across the kitchen. On the way, it knocked some dishes onto the floor and smashed them with what was described as 'unnecessary violence'. Ornaments in the house have been hurled across a bedroom, where they then collided with the bedpost and fell to the floor, often damaged. A large framed picture had to be taken down to prevent it from falling, but it was found five minutes later with the glass on it splintered – but the picture stayed still intact. A soup tureen lid once flew off mysteriously and was shattered against the opposite wall. There was a dish that strangely fell off the dresser on which it was placed and smashed on the floor. In another incident, a glass vase was moved off the mantelshelf by unseen forces and crashed to the floor, smashing itself. Things became so bad that the inhabitants of the house had to seek outside help.

First they tried the local vicar who came to the house to investigate. He tried blessing the property, but this did not help – he could make nothing of the situation and had to give up. The local police became familiar with the situation but they could find no human cause behind all these mysterious activities. Then the Council Engineer was called to examine the structure of the house to find out if there existed in it some vague vibration, which might cause the trouble. However, the poltergeist activity baffled him. He too had to admit defeat. A high church minister who was eventually told of the family's plight, visited the property to try to lay the poltergeist by performing a special service in the house. Poltergeist activity seemed to continue for a while afterwards in spite of this.

However, after a while, the trouble ceased of its own accord – as suddenly and strangely as it had begun. A number of writers on ghost stories nationwide have referred to this classic case of the Charlotte Street poltergeist, which was reported in some detail by both the local newspapers and the Devonshire Association.

Rum time at the Old Inn

A pub in St Budeaux, the Ferryhouse Inn, was said to have had more than its fair share of spirits – it was very haunted. The Ferryhouse Inn's new tenants found – soon after they moved in during 1993 – that they had at least two other-worldly regulars in their three-centuries-old Plymouth pub. They were the ghosts of an old woman and a young girl.

The Ferryhouse Inn's licensees, Derwin and Zoe Hawkes, had been told by their real-life regulars that the ghosts were part of the fittings of the pub. They had been appearing there for years. Mr Hawkes said, "We had been here for only a few weeks when we heard heavy footsteps on the stairs that link the two bars. I investigated and found nothing. Then the regulars casually told us it was the pub ghost. I wasn't convinced, but other things have happened since to make me believe we may be haunted. There have been occasions when the temperature in the bar has suddenly dropped and my deerhound has leapt up barking, his hackles up and his teeth bared."

The 300-year-old pub used to be a 'chop shop' where travellers on the Plymouth to Saltash ferry would stop for a brief rest, to get a meal. Mrs Hawkes believed the old woman ghost might have been a former tenant of the house. She said, "I have never seen them, but regulars tell me that the old woman used to live here. We have no idea who the young girl might be though. There are a lot of funny noises in the pub but you get used to them after a while. It's not frightening. I don't think they are threatening at all. It's not going to scare us away. They'll just have to live with us."

A most tidy ghost

Whisky, gin and vodka were not the only spirits to be found behind the bar in another 200-year-old Plymouth pub. For the Old Road Inn landlord Ray Doherty got an ethereal helping hand with the chores… from a tidy ghost with a passion for cleaning. Ray, a retired sailor, first discovered he had an unearthly helper shortly after he moved into the pub at Christmas 1992. He revealed, "The cleaning lady left a full bin of rubbish in the bar, and when she came back a couple of minutes later, it had been emptied. Since then, there have been all sorts of strange happenings – but nothing that has ever made me or the wife feel threatened. You will put something down on the bar, and two minutes later, it is behind you. It has happened to me when there was no one else in the bar, so I know it is not a prank. The odd thing is, it is mainly cleaning gear that the ghost moves about, as well as emptying bins. None of us has seen anything, but my sister-in-law Carol, who works here lunchtimes, says she can sometimes feel a presence."

Ray, who served 24 years in the Navy, said he was happy for the spirit to stay, but was keen to find out more about it. He told an *Evening Herald* reporter in August 1993, "I would like someone to enlighten me further about the history of the pub and why we should have a ghost."

Did the earth move…?

A Plymouth barmaid, Mandy Manley, who was living in St Budeaux when she worked at the Ford pub in Ford, certainly knows about ghosts in pubs. The Ford pub is said to have its own poltergeist called Old Joe. She said, "Pictures move and there are noises in the night. They say it's an old landlord. But nothing has happened while I've worked there."

At least this was less frustrating than another pub's mad monk, in the habit of regularly spiriting away all the pub teaspoons, making customers' digital watches flash, turning on the heating and interfering with the electrics – whenever the moon was full!

It was also less embarrassing than when another landlord called the police, thinking intruders were inside his pub playing skittles. Police blocked the roads with 12 patrol cars because there had been a spate of burglaries in neighbouring local pubs – but they only found that they had all been spooked. He said later, "My regulars have been telling me for a long time that my pub was haunted – and now I believe them."

Poltergeists!

In 1964, a Plymouth family moved into the ground floor flat of a 200-year-old house at number 31 Clifton Place. Soon afterwards, they began to feel as if they were under siege. Pieces of coal and coke began to fly around their rooms. The strange thing was that there was no coal present in the ground floor flat of this large house!

Such poltergeist projectiles are enough to unnerve anyone, and the resident family naturally felt alarmed by all these objects being hurled around them, hitting the bedpost and television set. By May and June that year, what began as coal and coke, progressed to several other items – their personal possessions were being dislodged from the mantelpiece.

They were not alone in such paranormal encounters. Their neighbours – the tenants in the two flats immediately above theirs – had also experienced weird happenings and had been complaining of coal throwing incidents. Together, they decided to seek help from a prominent local clergyman, who arranged to spend some time, between 11.15 p.m. and 12.30 a.m., in the ground floor flat. Within an hour of his arrival, he experienced the poltergeist phenomenon five times – and he knew there was no one else around responsible for this activitiy. "This has convinced me that there is a restless spirit in the building," he declared. "I didn't want to believe this but now I must. I am satisfied that it is a poltergeist."

The agent for the owners of the house, when told of the unwanted spectral presence, not only ridiculed the suggestion but dismissed it with considerable anger. "I am extremely annoyed about the whole thing," she said, and suggested that their "talk of a poltergeist is all rubbish – it's just someone playing a silly joke!" Following her furious outburst, the tenants received a month's notice to quit the property. The owners blamed the residents for all the damage that had been done to their property. They blamed the coal throwing on their tenants. A fortnight later, the Bishop of Exeter's chaplain performed an exorcism at the house, but the coal and coke still flew uncontrollably about.

Two of the families involved decided then to move out of their flats without waiting till their notice expired. The clergy helped out in a practical way by helping them to remove all their furniture to the nearby parish hall. The assistant to the vicar, the Reverend John Franks, said, "If the poltergeist is still in the house, we have entirely washed our hands of it. The house is now empty and although the church has by no means exhausted ways of exorcism, the vicar and I plan to do nothing more."

The incident was said to have been unusual, for although it was common practice for poltergeists to tamper with electrical appliances and throw things around, it was fairly rare for them to introduce their own props. However, as far as the victims and the vicar were concerned, the coke hurled at them was… 'the real thing.'

A more distressing experience happened to another victim – a single mother in her 20s. Jill said she had been suffering sexual advances from an amorous poltergeist every night for four months. She had tried to escape from the sex-mad spook, but when she tried to move from her haunted flat, she found her phantom attacker followed her to her new home. Jill had desperately sought help from all sources, including psychic researchers. "I have never seen anything," she said, "but I can feel it touching me. It crawls into the bed beside me. First it kisses me on the cheek and then it does all kinds of things. It is not violent, but when it makes love to me, it's truly vile. I decided to speak out when I discovered that other people have been sexually assaulted by entities from beyond the grave."

Psychologist Robin Furman, with a team of paranormal investigators, said, "This has all the signs of an incubus – a spirit which is consumed by a strong urge like hatred or sex."

Ghost made me do it!

A murder took place during the 1970s in one of the houses at Waterloo Street on Greenbank, in Plymouth. The guilty man not only admitted to the crime, but he also gave just about the weirdest reason for it – he claimed a ghost in the premises made him do it! Not surprisingly, the court ignored this and he was jailed for life. The court also ignored the fact that some months before the murder, a previous tenant had fled the house. He claimed he saw the ghost of a woman come down the stairs.

In Stoke there is another Waterloo Street, and just around the corner from this are eight houses known as Trafalgar Terrace in Devonport Road, running up to Nelson Avenue. These dwellings were built during the early 20th century, thus they were newer than the other property surrounding them.

In the late 1960s and 1970s, these houses were largely empty – people who lived in them before had been moving away, claiming that their homes were a harbour for ghostly activity. Near Trafalgar Terrace, there once used to be plague pits. People seeking reasons for the hauntings had suggested these manifestations could have emanated from those nearby plague pits. According to Mary Ann Penrose of Stonehouse, Plymouth, these houses come up for sale frequently and tend to change hands after a year or so of new ownership.

Poltergeist drove housewife to jail

Another case of a crime blamed on supernatural causes happened in June 1985. A young couple who had been married for only a year, were plagued by strange happenings at their home. Colin worked a night shift, leaving his wife, Julia, alone and terrified by poltergeist activity. "Lights had been turned on in the middle of the night and curtains drawn back and forth," she recalled. "The grandfather clock had been striking although it was broken. I found the colour TV turned to black and white, and my hairdryer and a fan heater mysteriously plugged in, and a cooker ring burning. Ornaments had been flying across the rooms, even a heavy paperweight. It had all depressed me so much, it started to affect our marriage. Colin and I started rowing when I refused to stay in the house – and this nearly wrecked our relationship."

Finally Julia, a sales assistant who had never been in trouble before, removed a cheque book from another woman's handbag, stole a cheque and forged her signature to cash £100. She then lied to her husband about the extra money she had – and when she was caught, she never even told him that she was appearing before the magistrates for her crime! She claimed she was doing all this so that she could be sent to prison in a drastic step to escape the poltergeist! In fact her defending attorney told the court at the time, "In her desperate condition, she committed this crime hoping she would be sent to prison and get out of her house." Instead, she was fined £100 and ordered to pay £100 compensation with £30 costs.

Julia said her local vicar had been to her house once to rid it of the ghost, "but that seemed to make things worse." She said, "As soon as he left, the lights flew on everywhere and there was a terrible smell of decay." Since her theft, she said, another 'exorcist' had been called in. She said, "We called in someone with psychic powers and he ran his hand over the floors and discovered a hot spot on our bedroom floor. He dug up a six-inch square of concrete floor and removed a very old, flat, rusty nail from that exact spot. Since then, things have quietened down and the house feels at peace."

A club and its ghosts

Harewood House in Plympton could boast more than 400 official members in November 1982… and a ghost – an elderly man in a red waistcoat and brown trousers. However, the apparition was said to have been there first. He goes back far longer than any members of the then newly-opened club…for the ghost is known locally. The unwelcome guest was described by the club owner, Keith Taylor, as mischievous rather than evil. He 'surfaced' soon after the club opened – when barman John Provenzano went to the cellar, which is refrigerated. And yet the cellar became stiflingly hot as he walked down the stairs. When he reached the bottom, he saw an old man wearing a red waistcoat and brown trousers…floating towards the ceiling. The barman was so frightened, he dropped everything and ran upstairs where he became physically sick. At the same time, the lights in the passage leading to the attic and basement went out. Plympton librarians decided to do some historical research to find some explanation for the weird happenings.

Keith Taylor recalled that on the club's opening day in May 1982, a window cleaner had told him that the top two rungs of his ladder snapped – and they had been checked regularly. "People in Plympton know that there is something here," Mr Taylor said. "Several times we have come in and felt this is not quite how we have left things." Mr Taylor remembered how, one evening before leaving the club, he had checked that all the doors were locked before he activated the door alarm. Then suddenly he heard "one of the doors slammed in the building and we wandered around trying to find out what had happened." He said, "There was no reason why a locked door should open and slam, or why the lights should not have worked when I tried them."

In fact, as far back as 13 December, 1951, G. W. Copeland had reported to the Plymouth Institution about three ghostly manifestations at Harewood House in Plympton. Mr Copeland reported: At 11 p.m., there could be heard a loud report that sounded like a pistol shot, from a certain room. No one has ever located a cause for this noise. There is one bedroom in the house where anyone sleeping in it had their bedclothes gently removed by invisible hands. The victim's clothes were deposited in a heap on the floor before morning. This was believed to be the work of a harmless poltergeist. There was also the small picture of a seascape, which persistently refused to hang on one certain hook. It always fell off that hook, although other pictures would remain on it. And the picture in question would stay on other hooks!

The supernatural presence in Harewood House became the subject of a clergyman's intervention on 17 November, 1982. A Roman Catholic priest, Canon Walter Costello – who had been priest in charge of Our Lady of Lourdes at Plympton for 16 years – said it was the first time since he had been at Plympton, that he had been called in to bless a house which contained a ghost or spirit. Canon Costello said afterwards that he saw or heard nothing during the blessing. As for the ghost of Harewood House, it had not been seen, heard or felt since.

Pipe-smoking phantom

A Plymouth woman, Daphne Searle of Beacon Park, needs no convincing about whether ghosts exist or not – she says she used to live with one. "There was a ghost in our house when we used to live in Camel's Head," she said. "An old man used to appear sometimes. I could see him and sometimes I would smell his pipe tobacco. He didn't like disturbance at all. He didn't like it if we moved any furniture. Things would go missing and they would turn up months later, and things would fall off the wall. At first I was frightened, but after a bit it didn't bother me. A neighbour said a man who used to live there would never leave the house. Once a visitor was lying in bed and the ghost touched him. He never slept there again."

Thumps that sound too plumb eerie

A plumber was working late at the works at Cattedown in Plymouth, one night during the 1970s, when he heard a bumping sound. He assumed a window must be loose and was tapping in the wind. So he checked every window in the building – but they were all secure. Thinking some other loose item was causing the noise, he made a thorough search, but to no avail. The noise persisted – and it sounded just like a man with a 'peg-leg' walking about. Nervous, he dashed to an acquaintance, who lived nearby. His mate came back to the building – and he heard the 'thump thump' as well. Together they tried to track down the cause… to no avail.

President's last meeting

Former *Evening Herald* history columnist Douglas Selleck used to tell a most intriguing story that took place in 18th-century Plymouth, when the White Ale Club met weekly "to drink punch, smoke tobacco, and talk politics". One night, the clubmen's talk was subdued, as their absent president was at the time in bed awaiting the grim reaper. Then, around midnight, this old gentleman himself came in silently, dressed in his nightclothes, and took his usual seat. He rested for a while, then without having uttered a single word, he rose and left the room. Greatly puzzled, the committee members dispersed, and early in the morning, they sent a deputation to the president's house, where they found out that he had died at about the time they had seen him enter the clubroom.

Douglas said, "for many years, this remarkable tale was told as an example of a well authenticated ghost story." He said, "One day, however, the late president's nurse, herself dying, sent for an apothecary, who was also a member of the club." She confessed to him that, while watching her patient on that fateful night, many years ago, she had fallen asleep and when she awoke, she found he had gone. "In a delirium, he had wandered off to his meeting. He arrived back shivering, lay down on his bed and died." When she was asked the next morning, she truthfully said he had died – but fearing her negligence had contributed to his death, she said no more. Douglas gleefully points out, "Thus, at least one ghost was finally laid to rest, without spoiling a very good story! "

A haunting on the Sound…

Another good old ghost story came from a woman whose grandfather was a Plymouth harbour pilot after the turn of the century. She grew up thoroughly familiar with the Plymouth coastline and the many ships that visited the Sound. She had seen them from her very own sailing boat – the pride of her girlhood. The woman in her seventies, Mrs Pillage – who died recently in a local old people's home – recalled one shipping tragedy that gained the reputation of being haunted.

It was a 1,000-tonne barquentine called the *Yvonne*, which hit the Plymouth Breakwater and sank in August 1920. Curious and an accomplished young sailor at the time, she naturally went out to investigate – and she took along her little Kodak Brownie box camera to photograph the sad wreck as it began slowly sinking. Mrs Pillage recalled that the site of the wreck was under surveillance by night watchmen who had complained about hearing bloodcurdling howls of unearthly things and the rattling of chains.

One night, two nervous guards decided to investigate the source of these weird noises. They courageously, albeit reluctantly, climbed onto the *Yvonne*. As they stepped on her deck, a steel marlin spike hurtled down from its mast and hit the deck just in front of them. This so completely terrified the duo that they immediately fled, abandoning their jobs, and were never seen again. Their annoyed bosses dismissed their claims as the rantings of a bunch of skiving workmen and paid no more attention to them or all the buzz about ghosts shooting intruders on deck with marlin spikes.

Then two days later, a local sail rigger, Mr Turner, came to the Breakwater to collect the tools that he had left behind when he recently went up to retrieve some gear from the *Yvonne*'s topmasts. He had left two marlin spikes in a bucket attached to the mast by a piece of rope. As he climbed up the mast, the stiff Devon breezes blew strongly across the Sound, and swept his hanging bucket against the rigging. This made a howling noise where it rubbed against the taut ropes – like the screech from some huge out-of-tune viola or cello… almost sounds spooky. Meanwhile the marlin spike rattled inside the iron bucket as the wind blew it from side to side, like chains being shaken together…

And later, on his way back, the spooked people there, who had been spreading various stories about the haunted *Yvonne*, heard Mr Turner complain loudly – about how he found one of his marlin spikes missing and wondered who took it from his bucket!

Phantom phone caller

Estate agents inevitably encounter all sorts of property as they go about their business. Their experiences can also range from the mundane to the most bizarre. One of the profession in Plymouth told this story to a *Western Morning News* reporter – of his strange experience that sent shivers down his spine every time he recalled the incident.

His agency was handling an empty property within the city boundary – built around the turn of the century – and any member of the staff deputed to visit this particular house always returned complaining that the atmosphere was rather unnerving. One day, when he had to be out at the house on 13 December, 1975, the telephone rang. He picked up the receiver – but there was no one there. As he hung up the receiver, he looked down and saw that the telephone wires were disconnected from the wall!

Grand spirit on the Hoe

Overlooking the Sound, at one of Plymouth's oldest hotels, the Grand on the Hoe, an upmarket spirit was said to walk the fourth floor. Porters who walked the corridors at night had talked of seeing a ghostly woman in Victorian dress. Receptionist Lucy Muldoon said, "The story goes that soon after the hotel was built, two men, an Italian and a Spaniard, were fighting over a woman. She died after they knocked her over the

bannisters during their fight – and she now haunts the fourth floor." She swiftly added however, "I don't believe it myself. I would have to see it to be convinced."

X-files from the vet

Evening Herald pets columnist, veterinary surgeon Nigel Taylor, is a fan of the 'X-files' TV series – but some of the weird things that took place in his animal surgery sounded as if he could have pulled them out from 'X-files' writer Chris Carter's scripts.

Firstly, there is supposed to be an elderly woman who haunts his consulting room Number Two. He has not encountered the spectre personally yet – but one of his nurses, Sarah, has. And another nurse, Lorna, used to hear someone calling her name when she was working alone in the practice early in the mornings.

Nigel Taylor also tells of a feline ghost. "We had to put a cat to sleep but he refused to rest in peace," he said. "The trouble was his owners went out and bought a new kitten. Then they noticed that every time they fed the new arrival, they could hear the old cat growling and spitting at it. The kitten was refusing to go near food – and worse was to come when it tried climbing the stairs in the house. About halfway up, something would fling it violently back to the ground floor. When the family heard dismembered voices calling the old cat's name, they decided enough was enough – and they came to me for help."

Well-known vet, Nigel Taylor

Nigel Taylor was not versed with the supernatural – but he knew someone who was… and this chap was able to perform an exorcism on site. The house itself is not at some out-of-the-way location – it is situated within half a mile from the noisy A38. Fortunately, his efforts worked and the old cat departed in peace. Once the rites were done, the new kitten was able to settle down – and life in the household returned to normal.

Not too far from here lived a close friend of Nigel's, in a Jacobean manor, on the edge of Dartmoor. He visited her one evening, and noted the strange atmosphere. "She didn't have to tell me but there were ghosts about," he said. Nigel recalled, "Most dramatic of all was a black dog who, for 20 years, had come every night into her bedroom and sat quietly upon her bed, vanishing at dawn. I've seen animals back away from rooms, sensing a presence in the gloom within. There are cows that won't stay in barns overnight but break out for freedom and for safety."

Plympton's Own Hairy Hands

Sightings of disembodied hands are horror stories that have made it to the newspapers, and such apparitions are by no means rare, although ghostly footsteps are the more usual cases, and partial apparitions more often tend to be floating heads or even eyes. However a demoniacal hand occurs in two old Scottish legends and there is a case of spectral hands appearing on the Trinité to Auray road in South Brittany.

Closer home, there were incidences reported in local newspapers in the 1970s, of a pair of 'hairy hands' striking terror into truckers driving on the old A38, past Plympton, near the eastern side of Plymouth. According to the English Tourist Board's *Good Ghost Guide*, several lorry drivers travelling on the A38 near Plympton at night have complained of a large pair of hairy hands clawing at their windscreens. One of these victims' wife gave a talk about it to fellow members of her Young Wives Association about his encounter. The old A38 was a frequent and regular nocturnal route for her husband, a long-distance lorry-driver. This was just before the opening of the new road – the continuation of the M5 motorway – and many nightshift drivers were wary of passing one spot outside Plymouth.

Until he experienced it himself, her husband had dismissed this as rumours even though several truckers claimed they had been startled by the sudden appearance of a hairy hand across the windscreen for a moment. However, this had not caused any accidents so far, and not much has been heard of it recently, since lorries now travel the three-lane stretch of the A38 outside Plymouth instead of the old road alongside it.

The old A38 hairy hands have a deadlier pair of cousins manifesting between Postbridge and Princetown – another spectral pair of Hairy Hands, which have been held responsible for many accidents.

A white belle and the bells

A lady recalled at a meeting of the Radford Park and Hooe Lake Preservation Society, that in her childhood, she had lived in Radford House – a 50-room mansion that was demolished in 1937 at Plymstock, where once Drake and Raleigh had been guests. The lady volunteered her first-hand account of strange happenings at the mansion in which she had lived for some time as a child – mentioning strange noises in the night, the ringing of bells which had been long ago disconnected, and the whimpering of dogs in terror, with their hair raised as if in fright at some unseen presence.

Surprisingly, many of the older generation who were present at that meeting, were able to corroborate her story at second hand. Some pensioners remembered stories of a railwayman who came off duty in the early mornings and used to cycle home through Radford Dip. One early morning, he saw the White Lady of Radford! There was another man who had worked through the night at the former *Western Morning News* offices at George Street. One day, while driving home just before dawn past the house, he too saw the pale spectre.

It was suggested that the illusion might have been created by the rising mist in the moist valley, distorted by the half-light of dawn. However, much had happened in the history of the house to give rise to such strange stories. Sir Walter Raleigh was held there under house arrest in the weeks before he was sent to his execution in the Tower of London, and there was bloody fighting at Radford House during the Civil War.

White Lady of Widey Court

The Countess of Mount Edgcumbe told a ghost story to the Mothers' Union of St Christopher's Church in Crownhill, Plymouth, in December 1953, that revived interest in the ghost of Widey Court – well after this White Lady had lost her home. Lady Mount Edgcumbe recalled when she first entered Widey, her initial thought was the understatement – "It's haunted."

Lieutenant-Colonel H. W. Markwick had made a gallant effort on the city council to save this historic ruin, but he admitted that he had never seen the ghost himself. However, he knew several people who had 'sensed the atmosphere' at the mansion on the outskirts of Plymouth before it was demolished in 1953.

One woman from Laira in Plymouth claimed in 1952 that she had seen the White Lady when her husband had been working on the estate and she had been 'frightened to death'. The apparition had actually appeared just half a century before.

Whatever the origin, a good ghost story, such as that of Widey Court, would always be exciting. The ghost of the White Lady was said to be that of a former daughter of the household. She was murdered on her wedding night by a jealous butler who had loved her in secret and could not bear to see her married to another man.

… And the rude guest

The ghost of Widey Court, which served the Royalists as headquarters during the Civil War siege, also took various other forms. There was a Grey Lady… and another ghost was reported, recalled by an old Plymouth woman who wrote to the *Western Morning News*, signing herself as 'O.M.' "It was somewhere about when I was born (1873)," she wrote. "The grandparents, Charles Burnard and his wife Jane, were invited to dine with the Algers at Widey. Grandfather for some reason could not go, so my Aunt Molly (who married a German two years later and died during the First World War) took his place. When they went in to dinner, the chair next to grandmother was empty (someone else had failed to turn up). She was very deaf. The dinner went off very well and they drove home in the carriage. On the way, she said, 'Molly, who was sitting next to me? A rude man, he never spoke a word.' Molly said, 'There wasn't anyone sitting next to you.' Grandmother then got very angry. She said, 'What nonsense, he was dressed in some funny kind of uniform.' She stuck to it, and insisted on Mrs Alger being asked. Her reply was, 'No one sat next to you. The chair was empty.' "

Although this happened in the year of her birth, 80 years before she wrote the letter, the old lady had many details, down to the name of the coachman and the horse. The 'funny uniform' might have been that of King Charles's officers, making this a far more exciting ghost than the slightly nebulous lady in grey or white.

Another ghost story connected with Widey Court told about a youth who, between 1888 and 1898, slept alone in a dressing room attached to the room where Charles I had slept. The lad liked to read in bed – though this was against strict regulations of the house – and his father used to walk down the long corridor late at night to make sure the light was off. One morning, after sudden rain, the youth noticed that some fresh linen, hung to dry near an open window, was soaked. He blamed this on the maids. He also asked his father why he had not bothered to shut it when he was walking down the corridor. His father said he had not walked down the corridor that night or on any other night during the preceding six months. Yet the youth was sure that someone had definitely been causing the floorboards outside his room to creak. The mystery of those ghostly footsteps was never solved.

Message on a floorboard

A Plymouth family was trying to solve a spooky riddle, over half a century old, that they uncovered under the carpet. This, they believed, could be linked to a ghostly spectre spotted at their home some years ago. Former Royal Marine Alan Gibson was working on some woodrot at his home in Meredith Road, Peverell, around September 1994, when he found a floorboard pencilled with a courteous message. It said: "Give this boy a shilling. August 11, 1944. Kenny Raymond, four-and-a-half years of age."

His wife, Linda, who was working in the *Evening Herald*'s property department, said, "I would love to find Kenny, who would be 54 by now, and give him a drink and his shilling." She was fascinated by the hidden history of her Victorian home, and hoped if she could have a chat with Kenny, this would help her find out more about her home – for her property had a ghost of a little boy, and she wondered if this had a connection with the message on the floorboard. Her 17-year-old daughter Andrea had reported seeing the little phantom. She said he was dressed in a school uniform with a cap and would stand by her bed sometimes, when she was younger. Andrea did not find the haunting sight frightening – and the spectre has not been spotted in recent years.

Ghost passenger of bus 19

A Plymouth bus conductor, Trevor Pearse, remembered the case of the bus service number 19 with great clarity. One day this double decker bus drew up at a stop on the main road into the city. "Two ladies, in their 30s, I should imagine, got into the bus, followed by two gentlemen," he said. "Up the stairs the four of them went. And there was another lady, rather older than the other ones, but as far as I was concerned, she was the mother of the two ladies, because the three of them looked so much alike. I assumed the men were the husbands."

As the older lady got on to the bus, for some reason she stopped and her face broke into a broad grin as she looked at Trevor Pearse. She gave a shrug with her shoulders and then walked upstairs. Trevor saw them as a party of five people who were simply getting on to his bus. The only thing that struck him as a little odd was the fact that the younger people had not been too courteous – they had left the old lady get on last. Later, when Trevor went upstairs to collect the fares, he noticed the old lady was no longer on the bus. "Where's the old lady gone?" he asked.

When the four passengers appeared baffled, he proceeded to describe her. "She was medium build, slightly smaller than medium height – I would have put her at five feet four," he said. "She was wearing – believe it or not – a leopard-skin two-piece suit with matching hat and handbag. And she had a diamond or diamond-like brooch in her lapel. Her hair was greyish, and very well groomed." He went on to say she was so similar to these two ladies, she must be their mother. Then one of the women told him, "The woman you've described to us was our mother. The outfit she was wearing was mother's. In fact, we bought it for her. Last time she wore it was when she went out with us. But she died 14 months ago…!"

DOCTOR, I CAN'T SLEEP

Insomnia: what it is, what to do about it

by Dr Adrian Williams FRCP

Amberwood Publishing Ltd
Park Corner, Park Horsley, East Horsley, Surrey KT24 5RZ
Tel: 01438 570821

PLANTLIFE

The Natural History Museum, Cromwell Road, London SW7 5BD

Registered Charity No. 328576

Amberwood Publishing supports the Plantlife Charity,
Britain's only charity exclusively dedicated to saving wild plants.

ISBN 1-899308-09-1

Cover design by Howland Northover

Typeset and designed by
Word Perfect, Christchurch, Dorset.

Printed in Great Britain

CONTENTS

Note to Reader

Whilst the author has made every effort to ensure that the contents of this book are accurate in every particular, it is not intended to be regarded as a substitute for professional medical advice under treatment. The reader is urged to give careful consideration to any difficulties which he or she is experiencing with their own health and to consult their General Practitioner if uncertain as to its cause or nature. Neither the author nor the publisher can accept any legal responsibility for any health problem which results from use of the self-help methods described.

About the author

Dr Adrian Williams FRCP is a consultant physician and director of the Baroness Lane-Fox Respiratory Unit and Sleep Disorders centre at London's famous St Thomas's Hospital. Previously Professor of Medicine at the University of California, Los Angeles and Director of the UCLA Sleep Disorders Centre, his work has encompassed all aspects of sleep medicine including research of sleep and it's associated illnesses. Dr Williams is the author, in particular, of many papers on obstructive sleep apnoea, and has been recognised by awards for his work in the field of sleeping disorders.

Foreword

"Oh Sleep it is a gentle thing
Beloved from Pole to Pole!"

So spoke Coleridge's Ancient Mariner. But gentle sleep can be elusive – and for some unfortunates this is often so. Sleep is a matter of everyday concern. "How did you sleep?" is the first question put by the anxious hostess greeting her guest in the morning. And requests for sleeping pills are all too frequent at the doctor's surgery.

Sleep remains something of a mystery, in spite of all the scientific studies and research that have been devoted to it Lack of sleep is a serious matter. It can ruffle our tempers, impair our efficiency and spoil our lives, and is a real menace if it affects our driving. Sleep deserves our proper attention, particularly when we are not getting enough of it.

This small book gives the reader a valuable insight into the nature of sleep and its disorders, especially insomnia. It reminds us that there are many common-sense remedies in our own hands. It gives us clear guidance on a simple system of self observation and self help which in most cases is sufficient for success. Commonly used drugs are described with their uses and limitations. The methods of complementary medicine too have an important place and a number of herbal and other remedies are effective.

The author is a doctor who has specialised in the scientific study of sleep and its disorders. From his experience he has given us here a clearly written and understandable account of a complex subject, with much good advice from which we all may benefit.

Dr John Cosh

1 | Sleep Disorders

We have long known that disorders of sleep are common. Formal epidemiologic studies have demonstrated that over 25% of adults have occasional or frequent complaints about sleep and that drugs are prescribed and used in connection with sleep more than for any other therapeutic purpose. Moreover, sleep problems appear to be associated with a risk of dying. It is well documented that more people die in the early morning hours than at any other time of day, presumably with some association to sleep. Further, there is a strong correlation between illness and how long an individual reports sleeping each night, with this increasing significantly at the extremes of four and ten hours. Although the nature of these relationships is as yet unclear, disturbances of sleep and alertness in some way impact upon survival.

In 1992 the results of a two year survey undertaken in the U.S. by the National Commission on Sleep Disorders Research was published and for the first time highlighted the large numbers of undiagnosed and untreated sleep disorders, pervasive sleep deprivation throughout society, and significant gaps in research. They felt that a root cause of all three appeared to be a virtual absence of education about these matters across all segments of society. This issue was taken up in the United Kingdom by the Royal College of Physicians who reported a year later on problems associated with sleep, focusing in this instance on the condition of sleep apnoea where breathing is interrupted and sleep therefore disrupted. However, as with the U.S. report, this document again drew attention to the pervasive nature of disorders in our society.

Consequences of poor sleep

In addition to influencing mortality, sleep disorders have an enormous impact upon quality of life. Millions of individuals live much of their lives in a fog of unrelenting sleepiness and fatigue. The medical, economic and social toll of sleep disorders is staggering. From the thousands of tired industrial shift workers who work when the brain is timed to sleep, to the accident victim who lost his fight to remain alert at the wheel (figure 1), to the elderly grandfather placed in a nursing home because of night-time

FATIGUE RELATED AUTO ACCIDENTS
Compiled Data

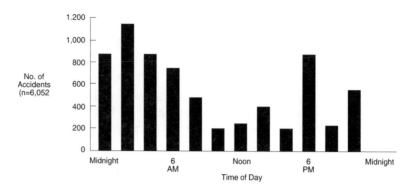

Mitler MM, et al. *Sleep.* 1988; 11:10

Figure 1
Analysis of over 6,000 fatigue-related car accidents shows
that the greatest risk is in the night hours, peaking at 2am.

wandering, to the sleepy child who once again fails at school, to the
grieving parents who have lost their sleeping child to Sudden Infant
Death Syndrome. For example, reduction of sleep time to five hours a
night for only two nights, significantly reduces physiologic levels of
alertness, impairs vigilance, and worsens athletic ability and creative
thinking.

Insomnia

Insomnia refers to the perception of inadequate or non restorative sleep.
Virtually everyone experiences occasional nights of insomnia that can
have significant effects on ability to function the next day. Moreover,
frequent or chronic insomnia, estimated to affect about one of every three
adults, is a severe problem for approximately half of those individuals.
Because recurring transient insomnia often becomes persistent insomnia,
detection and treatment are important in preventing chronic problems.

Insomnia varies with age and gender. The prevalence of insomnia is
approximately one and a half times higher in the elderly than younger
adults. Women are more likely to suffer from insomnia than men, with
typical prevalence estimates of 40% and 30% respectively.

Causes of insomnia vary and include acute or chronic medical problems, poor sleep hygiene (bed-time habits or routine), stress, and life-changing circumstances. Severe insomnia is a hallmark symptom of many mental and physical illnesses. In infants, sleep disturbances many be caused by colic or milk allergies, or by improper associations with sleep.

Insomnia is prevalent in those engaged in shift work. Studies suggest that anywhere from 40-80% of shift workers have difficulty sleeping. There is little question that the primary cause of such sleep disturbances is circadian disruption. In healthy adults, sleep tends to occur at a particular phase in the circadian course of core body temperature. Those who work the night shift must attempt to sleep at an inappropriate phase of the body temperature curve. As a result, the average sleep duration of night shift workers is 2-4 hours shorter than that of age-matched day workers.

Perhaps because insomnia is such a pervasive problem, it appears to be accepted as a normal part of life. However, there is abundant evidence that insomnia can have devastating effects on the careers and personal lives of those afflicted. Consistently restricted and fragmented sleep can lead to pathological sleepiness and potentially dangerous reductions in the ability to perform tasks. For example, insomniacs have twice as many car accidents as non-insomniacs.

For other afflicted persons, long-standing functional impairment results. Memory and cognitive dysfunction, poor interpersonal and coping skills, and a long list of illnesses are associated consistently with insomnia. Mistakes made by sleepy individuals may contribute significantly to accidents at work, including serious industrial accidents. Detailed examination of the daily activity of insomniacs has found that they spend about half as much time as non-insomniacs working or studying. Insomniacs are also more likely to report that they suffer from ill health and their work is limited by illness.

Despite the fact that Insomnia is the most common sleep complaint, few know how to approach or deal with insomnia appropriately. This applies particularly to doctors, two-thirds of whom when asked said they would prescribe sleeping tablets for a hypothetical elderly patient who suffered from chronic pain, did not exercise, was under psychological stress, woke up too early, and consumed caffeine close to bedtime, despite the fact that each of these conditions could and should be treated more directly.

When insomnia is found to be the product of a physical or mental problem, this sleep problem should be treated as a part of that disorder. When insomnia is the product of environmental factors, effort should be made to alter those factors and to provide treatment that is responsive to

DOCTOR, I CAN'T SLEEP

the causes of insomnia. A number of treatment options exist. For many behaviour therapy is the most successful and least invasive treatment. In such treatment, typically the patient learns proper sleep hygiene and, most important, the need for regular bedtime and wake-time. Relaxation training is also very effective, while bright light therapy – re-setting the biological clock by appropriately timed exposure to bright lights – is the most effective treatment for insomnia due to a delayed or an advanced internal clock.

2 | What is Sleep?

It is necessary to clearly understand the definition of sleep before we can clearly understand insomnia, its aetiology, consequences, and treatment. Sleep can be defined in several ways: a physiologic state of unconsciousness that is easily and completely reversible with stimuli; or, according to Stedman's definition, "a physiologic state of relative unconsciousness and inaction of the voluntary muscles the need for which recurs periodically". Sleep is a necessity of life and every human being must sleep in order to maintain proper function and health.

Healthy sleep – our current understanding

The most widely accepted definition of healthy sleep is that quantity and quality of sleep required to maintain optimal alertness during waking hours. While health researchers in other fields of scientific enquiry have made the accumulation of information their highest priority, this has not occurred in terms of human sleep. As a result, we have only the smallest idea of the range and distribution of human sleep requirements across society.

Normal sleep constitutes a portion of a cyclic circadian (about a day) alternation of sleep and wakefulness. This circadian sleep-wake rhythm is regulated by a neural pacemaker located in a region of the brain called the super-chiasmatic nucleus (SCN). The timing of the SCN is influenced by time cues, the most important of which is light and darkness, and controls many other (if not all) physiologic circadian rhythms, such as body temperature and various hormone secretion patterns.

Sleep actually can include two distinct states: non-rapid eye movement (non-rapid REM) sleep and rapid eye movement (REM) sleep. These states exist in virtually all mammals and birds. Scientific studies found that the sleep states are as different from one another as each is from the waking state. In adult humans, the non-REM sleep alternates cyclically with REM sleep approximately every 90-100 minutes throughout the night; non-REM sleep normally occurs first in the transition from wakefulness to sleep and occupies 75-80% of sleep. Non-REM sleep is subdivided into four stages that roughly parallel sleep depth; the lightest is called stage 1 and the deepest stage 4. The deepest stages of non-REM sleep are concentrated in the 90-minute cycles of the early part of the night. Brain function in non-REM sleep, markedly different from waking brain activity, continues to regulate and maintain vital body functions, often at a slowed rate (for example, heart rate and respiration rate). REM sleep which occupies 20-25% of sleep in adult humans, is characterised by a high level of brain activity, bursts of rapid eye movement, increased heart and breathing rates, and paralysis of all muscles except the diaphragm (to allow breathing to continue) and of course the eyes. It is an important defining characteristic of this sleep state and the loss of muscle tone detected during a sleep study is crucial to identification of REM periods. Some of us have experienced the residual effects of this paralysis as a momentary inability to move on waking (out of a dream as we often do in the morning), a phenomenon called sleep paralysis. REM sleep takes up an increasing proportion of the 90-minute sleep cycles in the later portion of the night; Eighty percent of arousals from REM sleep elicit vivid dream recall. The brain's regulation of bodily functions in REM sleep changes markedly as compared to waking or non-REM, certain functions – for example, temperature regulation – being inactivated or greatly suppressed in REM sleep. The major determinants of sleep, or influences on sleep are (1) inbuilt or *circadian,* (2) acquired or *homeostatic* and (3) *ageing*. The *circadian* effect is evident as a recurring pressure to sleep that is most evident as one might expect in the early hours of the morning about 4 or 5 a.m., and less intuitively, twelve hours later in the middle to late afternoon (see Fig 3 page 21). If individuals are encouraged to stay awake, unintentional naps will occur most frequently at this time. The sleepiness we often feel after lunch is a manifestation of this rather than the effects of food. These times of natural increased pressure to sleep are the same times when we are most at risk for sleeping if we are not fully rested. It is interesting that the 'bimodal' increase in sleep tendency exactly matches the distribution of frequency of motor vehicle accidents across the day where fatigue was blamed (and these are fully one-third of all road traffic accidents). Sleep is a drive state like hunger or thirst. The *homeostatic* influence on sleep is the equivalent of the need to recharge batteries. We can only spend so much time awake until sleep overcomes us. The reasons for this are not fully understood though interesting evidence comes from animal studies to suggest that a substance (substance S, the 'sleepy' substance) accumulates during wakefulness and ultimately promotes sleep. In the original experiment small amounts of cerebro-spinal fluid were removed from goats who were sleep deprived (goats were chosen for the ease of getting such a specimen) and injected into well rested goats who then proceeded to fall asleep. Very recently the nature of the substance has been better characterised with now a great potential for the pharmaceutical industry to produce a 'natural' sleeping aid. Although boredom may facilitate sleep, it does not cause sleep which only occurs if there is a biological need to sleep. In lectures I am wont to point out that it is not normal to fall asleep when I am talking; it is common, and predictable, but not normal! The final influence on sleep is that of *age*. As we get older the composition of our sleep changes with less slow wave or deep restful sleep at the expense of more light sleep.

Sleep disturbances affect the entire lifespan

Sleep disorders and disturbances occur at all points in the lifespan; babies, children, adolescents, adults and the elderly all experience sleep problems.

Sleep in the young is especially important during periods of growth and development, *children* and *adolescents* may be particularly vulnerable to the effects of sleep loss. Approximately a quarter of children between the ages of one and five experience some type of sleep disturbance, including sleep-talking, nightmares, sleepwalking, bed-wetting and night terrors. Childhood sleep disturbances tend to persist if untreated. Furthermore, children with sleep-waking disorders during the first year of life often experience multiple sleep problems in later years.

Although insomnia and sleep loss are prevalent in children and adolescents, the effects of these sleep problems on the young have not been established definitely. Sleep problems may be associated with difficult temperament in children. According to parents, children behave differently during the day after a poor night's sleep. Instead of appearing sleepy, the overtired child may appear overactive and inattentive. A label of 'problem child' may be applied early on; once made, it is difficult to shed. Poor sleep – childhood insomnia – may cause a child to be more vulnerable to physical illness, may limit parent-child bonding and later interaction, and may affect a child's self-esteem. Somewhat older children with poor sleep are more likely than those who are good sleepers to report negative emotional states, such as daytime tiredness, tension, moodiness and depressed feelings.

Sleep problems in the school-age child may move out of the bedroom and become a problem of daily life. The child may have difficulty concentrating in school and may develop secondary behaviour problems in the classroom. Children with inadequate or disrupted sleep often appear irritable, have decreased attention spans, are oppositional and can appear hyperactive. Children with primary sleep problems even may be mis-diagnosed as learning disabled or hyperactive.

A problem alongside childhood sleep disorders is family stress. Research has shown that parents of infants with sleep disturbances typically report more symptoms of depression, decreased satisfaction in their marriage, and greater anxiety in the parents of children with normal sleep patterns.

Sleep problems in adolescents span a number of specific disorders, including both disorders, in younger children and those more prevalent in adults. 75% of depressed adolescents suffer from insomnia.

Sleep in mid-life

Numerous sleep disorders appear during the second through to the fifth decades of life. During this period, most adults will experience an increase in work-load and family responsibilities. Insomnia associated with depression and chronic stress increases during these years. In addition, the body undergoes significant physiologic changes that may be accompanied by disrupted sleep.

Sleep disturbances occur along with post-partum psychosis and post-partum depression, disorders that affect 10-15% of women following childbirth. Little research has examined the sleep of pregnant women and new mothers, notwithstanding the fact that both sleep disturbances and mood alteration are prevalent in these two groups. Equally, only a limited number of studies have investigated the effects of maternal sleep disorders on the outcome of the pregnancy. Additional factors for both parents are the erratic sleep patterns of even the perfectly healthy new-born and the potential development of childhood sleep problems.

This age group suffers the highest incidence of insomnia related to shift work and other environmental stresses. The greatest number of shift workers are between the ages of 30 and 45. As we age, the disruption of rhythms is less well tolerated. Example, a college student can recover from sleep loss easily, but a middle-aged executive or shift worker, frequently cannot. Chronic sleep debt produces a loss of alertness and mental deficiency during the day, inappropriate mood, and more vulnerability to life's events.

The prevalence of insomnia in women over forty years of age is upwards of 40%, yet, we do not fully understand the chronicity nor the severity of such complaints. More than one-third of women are of meno-pausal age or older. During menopause, three quarters of women experience hot flushes and other physical symptoms that interrupt sleep, in some this sleep disruption causes insomnia, leading to excessive daytime sleepiness and fatigue.

Sleep in the aged

Altered daily sleep patterns are among the most prominent changes that occur with advancing age. These changes are so common that they are frequently mistaken as part of the normal process of growing old. However, new information indicates that many of these disturbances are not normal. They are, in fact, serious sleep disorders. Recent estimates suggest that over half of those now over the age of sixty-five experience some disruption of sleep including chronic and recurrent insomnias, and other sleep disorders such as limb movements during sleep or interrupted breathing.

Disturbances of sleep found in the older population may be the result of a variety of factors: retirement and changes in social patterns, death of a spouse and close friends and increased use of medicines. An older person's risk of developing depression appears to be greater among those suffering from insomnia than among those without insomnia. Moreover, ageing people frequently suffer from physical problems that are associated with disturbances of sleep. Over the course of the night, less sleep and less REM sleep is experienced. Daytime napping is increased as a form of compensation. Sleep problems in the elderly may result in the evening and night-time agitation, confusion, and disruptive behaviour disorder occurring in many demented individuals which become increasingly severe as the dementia progresses.

The importance of identifying and treating these problems is highlighted by the fact that 70% of people caring for older demented individuals cite the influence of nocturnal problems as a factor in the decision to place this person in an institution, often because their own sleep was disrupted. It has been found that among families of people who have been hospitalised, sleep disturbance and "troublesome" behaviour at night were among the most frequent problem relieved by placing that individual in a home.

3 | What is Insomnia?

"What I need is a good night's sleep". If that's your problem, you have lots of company. Trouble falling asleep or staying asleep – commonly termed insomnia – plagues one in three of us and is in the words of one Lancet article, a 'major cause of grief, misery and poor work' . It disturbs waking hours as well as sleep; after a bad night, most people feel sleepy the next day and have more trouble concentrating than usual. Insomnia presents a paradox: it's clear that troubled sleeping understandably may produce daytime fatigue. But why can't a sleepy person fall asleep fast at bedtime or sleep through the night? Fortunately, recent advances in understanding both the day and night components of insomnia enable the majority of troubled sleepers to be helped. Some people have trouble sleeping for just one night. Other people have trouble for many nights. The number of times you have trouble sleeping doesn't matter as much as whether or not the sleep problem has next-day consequences.

The cause of sleep problems may be physical, psychological, or both. Every-one has his or her own sleep-wake rhythm and disturbing that rhythm – either during the day or the night – can affect your sleep. We don't have to put up with another night of poor sleep! You deserve help – today!

Different kinds of insomnia

Insomnia can be broken down to three basic types. First, *transient insomnia*: transient means passing. So transient insomnia is very brief-lasting no more than several nights. It can usually be traced to a specific, recent event in our lives: a marriage upset, sleeping in a strange bed in a strange place or other such things. Then *short-term insomnia*: this type lasts up to two or three weeks. News that might affect us in an ongoing way such as job changes, divorce, serious illness, financial worries, or death in the family may be behind this sort of insomnia. Finally, *chronic insomnia*: chronic means persistent – poor sleep that continues for three weeks or more. About 10-15% of the population rate their sleep problems as being chronic and serious. There can sometimes be medical causes for chronic insomnia. It can also result from conditioning or developing bad sleep habits.

What causes insomnia?

Insomnia is a symptom, much like fever or stomach ache. Its causes include:

Psychological factors

Vulnerability to insomnia: some people seem predisposed to suffer insomnia in times of stress, much as others might suffer headaches or indigestion. Knowing that the problem may occur, and expecting that it will also subside, often helps people to weather bouts of poor sleep.

Persistent stresses: people with such problems as the troubled marriage, chronically ill child, or an unrewarding job, often sleep poorly. Psychological counselling can help here, enabling people to gain perspective on continuing troubles and exert more control over them.

Psychiatric problems

Insomnia, particularly with awakenings earlier than desired in the morning, is one of the most common symptoms of depression. People with anxiety, schizophrenia, and other psychiatric disorders also may sleep poorly. Treatment for the underlying disorder, usually involves both medicine and psychotherapy, often improves sleep (figure 2).

FACTORS AFFECTING THE DEVELOPMENT OF INSOMNIA

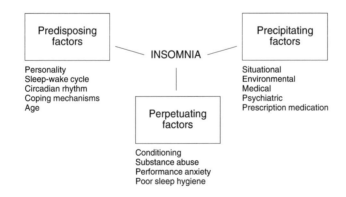

Adapted from Spielman AJ. *Psychiatric Clin North Am.* 1987; 10(4):541-533

Figure 2
The factors leading to insomnia can be classified into three main groups, Predisposing, Precipitating and Perpetuating, as indicated here.

Lifestyle

Use of stimulants: Even if caffeine near bedtime does not interfere with falling asleep, it may trigger wakenings later. Nicotine is also a stimulant; smokers take longer to fall asleep and sleep more lightly than non-smokers. Ingredients in many commonly used drugs, including non-prescription drugs for weight loss, asthma and colds, can disrupt sleep.

Use of alcohol: An alcoholic night cap may help induce sleep, but it also makes sleep more fragile throughout the night.

Erratic hours: Late hours on weekends as well as shift work schedules that demand frequent changes in sleep times may both undermine sleep. In contrast, regular hours help programme your body to sleep at certain times and stay awake at others.

Sedentary behaviour: The pendulum that fails to swing into full, active wakefulness during the day may also fail to swing into deep, restful sleep at night. This problem becomes increasingly common with age, particularly in people who also are ill.

Learned insomnia: Typically, people who sleep poorly in times of stress worry about not being able to function effectively during the day. They resolve to try harder to sleep at night Unfortunately, this determined effort often makes them more alert, setting off a new round of worried thoughts. Activities in and around the bedroom – changing into night clothes, turning off the lights, pulling up the blankets – soon serve as cues that prompt wakefulness. People who have trouble falling asleep in their own beds may fall asleep quickly when they don't intend to – reading the newspaper, for example, or watching television or driving. The predisposition to sleep poorly, even a few times a month, may be all it takes to maintain poor sleep, thus stress to find the persons continuing concern about it. Treatment of this type of insomnia aims to improve sleep habits and diffuse the accompanying anxiety.

Misuse or over-use of sleeping pills: If used every night, sleeping pills cease to benefit sleep after a few weeks. Abruptly discontinuing their use, however, may lead to a temporary worsening of sleep, a problem that can be minimised by cutting back gradually.

Environmental factors

Noise: Passing traffic, jet flyovers, a neighbours TV, and other noises disturb sleep even if you don't awaken completely. Mask sounds with a fan or air conditioner or by turning your radio to the static at the end of the FM band.

Light: Even when the eyes are closed, light comes through. If you don't want to get up with the sun or must sleep during the daytime invest in room-darkening shades or curtains.

Physical illness

Breathing disorders: Repeated interruptions of breathing during sleep may arouse a sleeper dozens, even hundreds, of times a night. These pauses may last as little as ten seconds, and as a result, go un-remembered in the morning. They are sufficient, however, to produce a perception of light or restless sleep. Severely disrupted breathing during sleep (the sleep apnoea syndrome) may affect people who breathe normally while awake; excessive relaxation of muscles necessary for breathing or trouble with the brain's control of breathing may occur only during sleep. Breathing-related sleep disruption becomes common with age. While most cases are mild and may not require treatment, it is generally wise to avoid sleeping pills, which may further worsen breathing. Severe cases may benefit from a new treatment, known as continuous positive airway pressure. It keeps the breathing passages open with a steady stream of air delivered through a mask worn over the nose during sleep.

Periodic limb movements: Brief muscle contractions may cause leg jerks that last a second or two, roughly every thirty seconds, often for an hour or more, several times a night. Like sleep apnoea, these may cause hundreds of mini-arousals and a perception of light sleep. Periodic leg movements also become more frequent and severe as people grow older. Treatment may involve sleeping pills and pain-relieving drugs. People who have an iron deficiency, particularly if they also experience a related daytime condition, restless legs, may benefit from iron replacement. Evening exercise and a warm bath often prove helpful.

Waking brain activity that persists during sleep: Some people who complain of light or non restorative sleep fail to sink fully into sleep, a fact that could be demonstrated when sleep is monitored throughout the night. Treatment has not yet been established.

Reflux: The back up of stomach contents into the oesophagus (properly called heartburn, because of the pain or tightness it produces in the mid chest area) can wake a person several times a night. When reflux occurs during waking, a few swallows and an upright posture rapidly clear the irritating materials from the gullet. Reflux during sleep, when swallowing is less frequent and posture recumbent, prompts waking with coughing and choking. Elevating the head of the bed on six to eight inch blocks may help prevent reflux; medicines can also provide relief.

19

Pain: Disorders such as arthritis, angina, lower back ache, head injury and hot flushes associated with menopause may upset sleep and waking hours. Sometimes positioning of pillows, type of mattress and pre-sleep behaviour can make a difference.

Medical differential diagnosis

The way in which your doctor might think of the cause of patient's insomnia will take account of these predisposing, precipitating and perpetuating factors but will usually consist of the following:

1 Medical causes: any disease that causes discomfort or breathlessness may cause insomnia.

2 Psychiatric causes: sleep can be disturbed in many psychiatric disorders. While the severity of the insomnia usually reflects the severity of the psychiatric problem, this is not always the case. For instance, bad sleep habits that develop during the time of depression may continue after the depression has been treated.

3 Drugs that can cause insomnia: the two most commonly used drugs that cause insomnia are alcohol and caffeine. Although alcohol is a powerful hypnotic, it wears off quickly, typically causing awakenings and sleep fragmentation in the latter half of the night. Caffeine may have a long half-life in some, so that coffee, tea or cola can prevent sleep onset at night. Other drugs such as decongestants and nicotine are used commonly enough to be troublesome whilst various other medicines that might be prescribed such as blood pressure medicines or breathing tablets may be relevant.

4 Behavioural causes: behavioural causes of insomnia are in and of themselves frequent and also commonly complicate other causes of insomnia. The separation of behavioural causes into psychophysiological insomnia and poor sleep hygiene is somewhat artificial. Most patients with psychological insomnia have problems with sleep hygiene.

Psychophysiologic insomnia is the most frequently made diagnosis in patients complaining of insomnia who are seen by sleep disorders specialists. It is a kind of learned or a conditioned response to the sleep environment. Many patients show evidence of somatic or cognitive arousal to the bedroom or sleep. They worry about their ability to sleep and their ability to perform if they do not sleep. They frequently sleep well at times and in places where sleep is not expected.

Poor sleep hygiene is common in our society and, in part, stems from a lack of knowledge about the physiology of sleep. The irregular sleep schedules and excessive napping are particularly common in those not constrained by work schedules. Caffeine and alcohol are ubiquitous disturbers of sleep. The entertainment industry conspires to stimulate us when we should be relaxing.

5. Circadian Rhythm Abnormalities: The advent of easy artificial illumination has brought with it the ability to fool our internal time keeper (and to allow poor sleep hygiene). Of the three circadian rhythm disorders causing chronic insomnia, delayed sleep phase syndrome (where the internal clock is shifted so that sleep onset is delayed) and shift work are the best described. To this one might also add jet lag, but it is seldom a cause of chronic insomnia. Figure 3 illustrates the normal circadian variation in sleep tendency. We fall asleep least readily in the morning and early evening (longest latency) but much more readily during the night hours, and to as less extent after lunch (shorter latency).

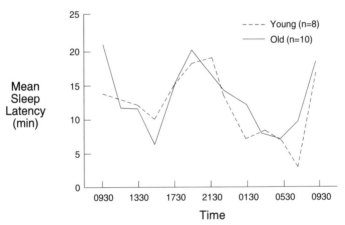

CIRCADIAN VARIATION IN SLEEP TENDENCY
Function of Time of Day

Richardson GS, et al. *Sleep.* 1962;5(suppl 2):582-594.

Figure 3

The normal variation in sleep tendency throughout the 24 hours, showing the greatest tendency to sleep being in the night hours (shorter latency). There is also some tendency to sleep in the afternoon, more marked in the older subjects than in the young.

In the advanced sleep phase syndrome the internal clock says it is time to sleep in advance of the desired sleep time. The patient is too sleepy in the early evening, falls asleep too early, then awakens too early the next morning. This circadian disorder is most common in the elderly.

In the delayed sleep phase syndrome, the internal clock is set earlier than the environmental time. If the desired bedtime is 11.00pm the circadian clock may be telling the brain it is only 6.00pm. The circadian sleep phase is thus delayed by a few hours. The patient cannot fall asleep, in this instance until 3.00am, and cannot wake up fully until perhaps 11.00am, long after school or work has started. This problem tends to be complicated by poor sleep hygiene and be more common in the young. It may account for 10% of sleep onset insomnia.

Shift work is a particular problem for night shift workers and for those with rapidly rotating shifts. Because of the overwhelming influence of light on the circadian pacemaker, the adaptation to night shift rarely, if ever, occurs. The ability to tolerate shift work decreases with age.

6. Primary Sleep Disorders: These are the conditions that are considered the medical problems of sleep and include periodic limb movements in sleep, often accompanied by the sensation of restless legs before sleep, and sleep apnoea syndrome. In both these the phenomenon in question i.e. leg movements or apnoeas cause arousal from sleep which may not be remembered as such but which may cause a sensation of non restorative sleep or indeed frank awakenings interpreted as a difficulty with sleep maintenance.

Insomnia axioms

• Sleep can be wilfully denied, but not wilfully obtained.

• Arousal takes precedence over sleep.

• The time course of arousal is rapid; of relaxation, slow.

• Insomniacs are adept at creating and internalising threats.

• The longer insomnia lasts, the worse it gets.

The harder we try to sleep, the less we are able to sleep. Sleep only comes when we don't really care. Arousal takes precedence over sleep. In a conflict between the need to sleep and the need to stay aroused, arousal usually wins. To be able to sleep, we need to feel safe and slightly bored. The time course for arousal is rapid, of relaxation slow. Once we are aroused, it may takes many minutes to slowly calm down again. Insomniacs are adept at creating and internalising threats. Things that others can set aside and worry about tomorrow, the insomniac has to take care of before sleeping. The longer insomnia lasts the worse it gets because perpetuating factors come into play and the initial factors may no longer be important.

Although a principal cause of insomnia can be found under the five categories discussed, more often than not more than one cause is operative in maintaining the inability to get to sleep or to stay asleep.

4 | Evaluation of your sleep – a two-week sleep diary (appendix)

Measuring how you sleep and its effect on your day

Before your sleep can be corrected, it is important to determine exactly what your sleep is like now. It is best to do that by looking at your sleep patterns over many nights, rather than on a single night. You may wish to record the quality of your sleep over ten to fourteen nights using descriptions such as bad, poor, fair or good for those particular nights.

It is also important to understand how you are feeling during the day and the level of your functioning and in the same way it is useful to record roughly how you felt during each of the days in question. For this one might record separately for the morning, afternoon and evening whether you are very sleepy, sleepy, foggy, alert or very alert.

The importance of this exercise may be self evident. If daytime function is adequate (no falling asleep watching films, in front of a television, or driving, not being irritable or unable to concentrate) one may be a short sleeper and not an insomniac. It is permissible to curtail time in bed to the hours that one seems to need for adequate daytime functioning.

DAILY SLEEP LOG

To understand your sleep problems you need to note the times when you sleep, nap and wake-up during sleep. In addition the times when you drink coffee, tea and alcoholic beverages. If medication is taken, also record this. It is important to keep a record for 7 days and each column represents a new day (the first column is an example).

Keeping a sleep diary may help you understand where a possible problem lies i.e. too many stimulating drinks or too much sleep during the day. This information may also assist your doctor.

Date	Ex. 7/2	Mon	Tue	Wed	Thurs	Fri	Sat	Sun
Total night's sleep	3 hours							
Bedtime	11.00P							
Time of final awakening in the morning	5.30A							
Estimated time it took to fall asleep	45 min							
Time of awakenings during sleep and length of time you were awake	2A–1hr 3A–1hr							
Naps, times you napped, and length of naps	2P– 45 min							
Medications taken, times, and amounts	Dalmane 30mg 10.30P							
Coffee and tea, number of cups and time drank	7.00A–1							
Alcoholic drinks, number and time drank	8.00P–1 9.00P–1 10.00P–1							

Evening Activities for Day:

1. _____

2. _____

3. _____

4. _____

5. _____

6. _____

7. _____

Date	Ex. 7/2	Mon	Tue	Wed	Thurs	Fri	Sat	Sun
Total night's sleep	3 hours							
Bedtime	11.00P							
Time of final awakening in the morning	5.30A							
Estimated time it took to fall asleep	45 min							
Time of awakenings during sleep and length of time you were awake	2A–1hr 3A–1hr							
Naps, times you napped, and length of naps	2P– 45 min							
Medications taken, times, and amounts	Dalmane 30mg 10.30P							
Coffee and tea, number of cups and time drank	7.00A–1							
Alcoholic drinks, number and time drank	8.00P–1 9.00P–1 10.00P–1							

Evening Activities for Day:

1. _____

2. _____

3. _____

4. _____

5. _____

6. _____

7. _____

5 | Behavioural treatment and sleep hygiene

Sleep hygiene refers to those things one can do for oneself to help improve sleep. It can be done by the individual in the home without complex equipment or training. Much of it, but not all, is common sense. There are almost no sleep hygiene rules that apply to everybody. The patient should try sleep hygiene rules in a careful, scientific manner using sleep logs. They should try one rule for a week, then not use the rule for a week. Every morning the patient should write down how they slept: how long it took to fall asleep, how many awakenings, how long they slept and how refreshed they felt in the morning. For example, they might take a nap every day for a week and write down how they slept at night. Then, they do not take a nap for a week and write down how they slept. Compare the two sleep logs and determine whether, in this case, daytime naps should be avoided. Often the particular thing that helps sleep in a given individual is highly idiosyncratic.

Some basic rules for good sleep

Here are eleven proven rules that have helped many people not only sleep better, but feel better when they wake up. This is good advice for everyone.

1 Sleep only as much as you need to feel well rested during the following day: stretching out your sleep is not a good idea. Oversleeping weakens the power of sleep to leave you feeling refreshed. It also resets your natural "biological clock". By oversleeping you are likely to have trouble sleeping the next night.

2 Keep a regular sleep schedule: keep as regular a sleep schedule as is reasonably possible by going to bed and getting up at the same time both weekdays and weekends. This will help you develop a regular sleep-wake rhythm.

3 Do not work at falling asleep: when sleep does not overtake you, don't force it. This just creates anxiety that keeps you awake. Get out of bed and do something different for a while. Return to bed when you feel drowsy.

4 Reduce unwanted noise and light in your room: aeroplanes, car traffic, and unwanted music and light can disturb and lighten your sleep even if they don't wake you. You may want to investigate ways to minimise the unwanted sounds in your bedroom. Earplugs or even low level background sound may be helpful.

5 Keep your bedroom at a temperature in a comfortable zone for you: a too warm or a too cold room can disturb and interrupt your sleep.

6 Do not go to bed hungry: a light snack before bedtime may help you fall asleep, as well as prevent hunger pangs that can wake you during the night. But don't over eat before you go to bed either. Indigestion can wake you up, too.

7 In the evening, do not drink beverages that contain caffeine: even if you don't feel it, caffeine – whether from coffee, tea, colas or chocolate – disturbs your sleep.

8 Avoid the bedroom clock: clock watching kills sleep. Finding out what time it is always causes an emotional reaction – it is either later or earlier than one thinks. Set your alarm clock and hide it in the top dresser draw and take off your watch. Most people sleep better away from time pressures.

9 Exercise about six hours before bedtime: it has been shown that during the night insomniacs do not decrease their core body temperature and their metabolism as much as normal sleepers do. Aerobic exercise of at least twenty minutes duration causes an increase in core body temperature and metabolism, followed by a rebound decrease about five or six hours later. This decrease helps sleep. Therefore exercise in the late afternoon or early evening is best. Exercise in the morning or just before bedtime will not help.

For those who cannot increase their metabolism by exercise it appears that passive heating in a hot bath is similarly effective. However, this passive heating is done best one to two hours before going to bed.

10 Deal with worries before bedtime: if you are prone to worry in bed, try and reserve some time in the evening to make a list and decide for each worry what can be done about it tomorrow.

11 Do not try all of these rules simultaneously! In the best case, you will sleep better, but not know why. Much more likely, try each rule haphazardly and nothing will work. An important aspect of changing sleep hygiene is a need to break up current sleep behaviours, because they are associated with insomnia. It sounds so simple, but sleep hygiene really works in many cases.

Behavioural approaches to insomnia treatment

The treatment of choice for chronic insomnia is behavioural therapy. Although such therapy takes considerable time, there are numerous studies now suggesting that it is effective and lasts for years. Behavioural therapies that are part of this approach are, along with sleep hygiene, sleep restriction, stimulus control therapy and relaxation training.

Sleep restriction

Sleep restriction therapy rules

This form of behavioural therapy is based on the observation that the more one curtails sleep, the shorter the time to fall asleep, the fewer arousals one observes at night and the deeper sleep becomes. The method is not easy on the insomniac, who needs considerable support while undergoing this therapy. One would compute sleep efficiency (total sleep divided by total bed-time) and based on moving averages of five nights, one would increase bed-time by fifteen minutes if subjective sleep efficiency is better than 85%.

It is another proven method that can really help. If you have difficulty falling asleep, if you lie in bed worrying about falling asleep or wishing you could sleep, sleep restriction is a good method for you to practise. Sleep restriction is actually very simple. What you do is limit the time you spend in bed to the time you normally spend sleeping. If you decide to practise sleep restriction, remember, that you must be patient. Give the method time to work – at least two to four weeks – before you judge its effectiveness.

Sleep restriction is a system designed to make you a more "efficient" sleeper meaning that more of the time you spend in bed will be time asleep. Although sleep restriction sounds as though you will be getting less sleep, you will eventually be getting more sleep. During the first week or two of practising sleep restriction, you may feel some daytime sleepiness. This is normal for many people learning sleep restriction, and actually it is a sign that it is working. You may not be getting enough sleep, but the sleep you are getting is deeper and more consistent, and eventually will be more refreshing.

Restricting your time in bed

Sleep restriction is limiting the time you spend in bed to the time you spend sleeping. Here is how to get started. Determine how many hours you actually spend asleep on your average night. Lets say it's five hours. Then determine how many hours you spend in bed. Lets say it's seven hours. So two hours on average each night is spent in bed without sleeping.

The next step is to take two hours off your bedtime. So, for example, if you normally go to bed at 11.00pm and lie in bed for two hours trying to sleep you will now go to bed two hours later. In this example you will get into bed at 1.00am. It is always best to get up at the same time so go to bed later, instead of getting up earlier. While you are practising sleep restriction you will need to keep track of your "sleep efficiency" so, for the next two weeks, just take a few minutes each day to fill out a sleep diary such as the one mentioned before.

Adding time back to sleep

The final objective of the sleep restriction exercise is to start increasing the amount of time you are actually asleep while in bed. When you are first learning the technique, it is easier to achieve your goal of 85% sleep proficiency by limiting your time in bed only to the time you normally spend asleep. As you get better at this exercise, you can start to increase you time in bed by fifteen minutes. For example, if your sleep efficiency has reached 85% for five nights in a row, you can now add fifteen minutes to your bedtime. In other words, you go to bed fifteen minutes earlier but you must still get up at the same time. The more you practise this technique, the better you will become at it and you will become a more efficient sleeper.

Stimulus control

Making your bed a better place to sleep

A stimulus is a signal or cue in the environment. For example, the kitchen table may be a stimulus for eating. Just by sitting at it, our mouths may water and our stomachs may gurgle, even when there is no food in front of us. The bed should be used almost exclusively for sleep (sex is an exception). When you lie down on your bed it should act as a stimulus to help you fall asleep. But too many people organise much of their lives around their beds. They do their book work there. They read, play cards, eat, watch television – all in the very place that should be reserved for sleep. There are some very simple common proven guidelines to stop those feelings of being energised away from your bed. These include:

1 Lie down only when you intend to go to sleep, only when you feel sleepy.

2 Do not use your bed for anything but sleep and sex.

3 Ten minutes is the maximum you should lie awake while trying to sleep (twenty minutes for those over sixty). Don't stare at the clock. Use your internal clock to signal when roughly ten minutes has passed.

Remember the bed is for sleep, not for worrying. If you can't fall asleep get up and go to another room. Only return to your bed when you again feel sleepy.

4 If you still can't fall asleep, repeat this step as often as necessary.

5 Set your alarm and get up at the same time every morning, regardless of how much you've slept the night before.

6 Do not nap during the day. You should only nap if that has always been part of your daily lifestyle. Even then, you should nap at the same time every day, and keep it short – less than an hour.

Remember, good sleep comes from establishing a consistent sleeping pattern.

Stimulus control therapy rules

These rules are the following:

1 Go to bed only when sleepy.

2 Use the bed only for sleeping, do not read, watch TV or eat in bed.

3 If unable to sleep, move to another room. Stay up until really sleepy.

The goal is to associate the bed with falling asleep quickly. This last technique is probably the best researched behavioural therapy on insomnia. By now there are at least twenty-five solid outcome studies using this treatment method. Wherever stimulus control therapy is compared with any other treatment, it is either superior to other treatments or at least equal to them. The basic idea behind stimulus control therapy is the thought that for most insomniacs the stimulus surrounding sleep (bedroom, darkness) have become conditioned to tension and arousal. The goal is to re-associate these stimuli with relaxation and sleep.

Progressive relaxation

Many of us tense up without wanting to because of physical or emotional stress. Even though our conscious minds may have learned to tune out our muscular tension, it still affects our sleep. Ironically, the first step towards becoming less tense is to become more so. By deliberately causing our muscles to tighten, we learn how to feel, then produce, the opposite sensation, relaxation. Give yourself fifteen minutes twice a day and practice the following techniques.

Relaxation training

The type of relaxation technique is less important than that it be done very thoroughly. An individual has to use these techniques at sleep onset, i.e. at a time when consciousness and control fade. Therefore, doing these techniques has to be automatic so that you do not have to consciously think what to do. While it makes intuitive sense that insomniacs are tense and need to relax, is a small group of insomniacs (10–30%) were able to relax quite deeply and still cannot fall asleep. If you try newly learned relaxation technique at sleep onset before the technique is practised, it is unlikely that it will help. This then results in another failure experience. Therefore, forbid yourself to use the relaxation skill until you have evidence that the skill is developed. This typically is assessed either by feeling unusual sensations when relaxing (feelings of lightness, warmth,) or when you are unable to maintain wakefulness during relaxation sessions. Such relaxation exercises include abdominal breathing which is a relaxation technique that is easy to learn. It is based on the demonstration that thoracic breathing is active and tense while abdominal breathing is comfortable and relaxed. The steps to abdominal breathing are to practice abdominal breathing without any movement in the chest. At a short pause after each breath, contemplating the previous breath's smoothness, regularity and comfort.

In summary, although none of the behavioural techniques are very hard to administer, they do take considerable time and some skill. However, these three major behavioural approaches do work given time.

Disease oriented treatments

For those insomnias known to be caused by a specific disorder, a specific therapy will be indicated. These disorders will include the restless legs syndrome and its accompanying periodic limb movement disorder, circadian rhythm disturbances and depression. Specific medications are helpful in the restless legs syndrome and periodic limb movement disorder and can be prescribed by your doctor.

For the circadian rhythm disturbances i.e. delayed and advanced sleep phase syndromes, there is a need to set one's clock to be more synchronous with the environment. For the delayed sleep phase syndrome there is a need to set the clock ahead. To achieve this bright light in the morning is needed. To obtain this stimulus, at the time of year that it is light early enough, being outside in the daylight will be helpful. However, sufficiently intense exposure is unlikely at 6.30 or 7 o'clock in the morning so that a light box may be needed. This can be again obtained through a doctor interested in sleep disorders. The importance of good sleep hygiene, especially a regular sleep schedule, cannot be over-emphasised. In the advanced sleep phase syndrome the circadian clock runs ahead of the environmental time and needs to be set back. Bright light in the late evening may be helpful. Again a regular sleep-wake schedule must be followed.

For insomnias related to depression it may be possible to relieve insomnia immediately using a sedating antidepressant. If sedating antidepressants are poorly tolerated then the option would be for using a non-sedating equivalent along with a brief trial of a sleeping agent or hypnotic.

Pharmacological treatment

Can sleeping pills help?

Although sleeping tablets are frequently prescribed by doctors for insomnia, such treatment should not be the mainstay of management for most of the causes of disturbed sleep. It is generally believed, however, that short-term intermittent use of hypnotics and sedatives may be useful for temporary problems such as bereavement, but it should be stressed there are no studies that demonstrate their long-term effectiveness. It is interesting that the practice of hypnotic prescription use actually parallels the recommended pattern. 74% of individuals who took prescription sleeping pills in the last year took them for less than fourteen nights in a row. There are of course a few people taking them for months at a time. However, there is a segment of the population (11%) which takes them nightly. Most of these individuals have been doing this for a long time. The frequency of such use is not equally distributed in the general population. More women then men receive hypnotics and the elderly receive more hypnotics than their younger counterparts. What is reassuring about this information is that the demographic distribution of hypnotic use parallels the demographic distribution of insomnia complaints.

The drugs most commonly prescribed are Benzodiazepines, which carry varying and serious risks of dependency, tolerance and rebound insomnia and although a new generation of hypnotics offers fewer risks, even these aren't recommended for longer than several days.

Sedating Antidepressants: Although they are not indicated for sleep, sedating antidepressants such as amitriptyline, doxepin, trimipramine, and trazodone are sometimes used by clinicians to treat insomnia especially if the cause of the insomnia is depression. Their efficacy in chronic insomnia has not been proven. These drugs must be evaluated by the clinician based on a benefit:risk ratio that includes the onset of action (which may be days or weeks), possible side effects, and the incidence and consequences of intentional or accidental overdose. Sedating antidepressants are usually contraindicated in the elderly and in patients with cardiovascular diseases, and they may cause significant impairment of psychomotor functions. Tricyclic antidepressants exhibit significant adverse effects including a disturbance of heart rhythm, drop in blood pressure causing faintness on standing, daytime sedation, and a dry mouth. Amitriptyline, doxepin, and desipramine are tricyclics. Doxepin has a high incidence of adverse events including amnesia. Trazodone hydrochloride kinetics are characterised by biphasic elimination from the body (first phase at 3-6 hours, followed by a second phase from 5-9 hours after administration) which may lead to significant accumulation. Significant adverse events with trazodone include daytime sedation, nausea and weight gain.

Complementary Medicine
With orthodox medicine providing only a temporary fix, and sometimes carrying the risk of addiction, many people turn to complementary medicine for help with sleeping. The best known form of complementary medicine is the use of herbal remedies.

Herbal medicine could well claim to be a part of orthodox medicine as, for centuries, herbs formed the basis of most medical treatments, and every physician used to have a working knowledge of herbs and their uses. Of the many herbs having sleep enhancing powers, *Valerian* is the best known. A number of constituents have been isolated from its root, but how much each contributes to its sedative effect is still undecided. Extract of Valerian root has repeatedly been shown to improve sleep by shortening the time to onset of sleep and improving its quality. It is safe, and leaves no morning "hangover". *Passion flower* (Passiflora) too is a sedative herb with a longstanding reputation, and other helpful herbs include *Hops, Camomile, Lemon Balm, Californian Poppy, Lime tree flowers* and *Wild lettuce*. Camomile and Lime flower are popular as infusions (tisanes) but Valerian, with its disagreeable taste is generally taken in tablet form. A number of herbal tablets combine Valerian with other sedative herbs in various proportions. As a rule, owing to their gentle action herbal sedatives are best taken some time before bedtime, and they are less useful as a "knockout" during the night if sleepless hours have already passed. More detailed information can be found in a companion book to this one: "Herbal Medicines for Sleep and Relaxation" by Dr Desmond Corrigan.

Aromatherapy too has a long and respectable pedigree, making use of essential oils of herbal and plant origin that have been known for centuries, and studied in more detail in recent years. Oils recommended for their relaxing and sedative effect include *Lavender, Neroli and Ylang ylang*. A few drops are added to a hot bath before bedtime. If used for massage the pure oil should be diluted, mixing 3 or 4 drops with an eggcupful of sunflower or almond oil. Self massage with warm oil is helpful for the neck, shoulders and upper arms and legs, and if a friend or partner is available to help. the shoulder girdle muscles and back can be massaged as a preliminary to sleep.

Homoeopathy is based on the principle of "like curing like", i.e. giving, in a specially prepared and highly diluted form, a remedy which in far bigger doses would cause the symptoms that are complained of. Moreover, the remedy should be matched to the patient's nature as well as the details of the complaint. This ideally means having a careful prior assessment from a trained homoeopath. The remedies most often given for insomnia are *Coffea* (for the overactive mind), *Arsenicum album* (where there is apprehension and restlessness) and *Ignatia* (where there is sadness and grief). The usual strength or "potency" given is 6, and the tablet is allowed to dissolve under the tongue, and not swallowed.

Relaxation has already been mentioned on an earlier page, most simply practised while sitting back or lying comfortably and consciously relaxing limbs and trunk in a gradual and upward progression. Slow, deep breathing at the same time is helpful. This can be combined also with *Visualisation* of some calming tranquil scene or memory. Some *Yoga* techniques focus particularly on relaxation and are helpful when practised before sleep; a training session with a teacher beforehand is advisable. *Autogenic training* is another technique employing conscious relaxation, limb by limb, based on autosuggestion, and can be helpful before sleeping. *Shiatsu* is a Japanese form of manipulation in which the therapist applies firm pressure by hand or with fingers at specific points on the body. Derived from this is *Acupressure* in which you can apply finger pressure yourself at certain points; those recommended for encouraging sleep are on the top of the head in the midline, at the base of the skull at the back, close to and either side of the midline, and at the base of the spine close to the midline at the level of the fifth lumbar vertebra.

6 | Special issues

There are many aspects of life which affect sleep, some quite normal, for example *pregnancy,* or sufficiently common to be considered normal, for example *snoring,* along with *travel across time zones.* The very fact, however, that they are considered normal or near normal makes the effects that they have on sleep also fall into what is considered to be the normal experience. A moment's thought about this however suggests that this is not necessarily the case.

There is the woman who during *pregnancy* suffers the discomfort of the large abdominal 'tumour' which prohibits sleeping on one's back and is associated with frequent arousals during the night, if only with the need to pass urine. In folklore it has been said that this is good preparation for the time immediately after birth and during the infant's first year when its sleep is fragmented. This should not however minimise the likely effect on the day and on the fabric of the household!

A similar issue may be made about *snoring* which affects fully a third of men, and indeed a half of those over the age of forty-five are believed to snore habitually. The intensity of the snoring is very variable but may be loud enough to promote deafness in the bed partner when heard over a long period. The Guinness Book of World Records now has a section for the world's loudest snorer who has clocked in at 97 decibels, or something like a Mac Truck rolling down the road outside your house. Snoring of this intensity, even if it doesn't disturb the snorer, is well known to disturb the bed partner and therefore deserves attention. It also may deserve attention itself since snoring is a marker for the presence of disturbances of breathing during sleep. To understand this it may be worth commenting on the mechanism of snoring. Snoring is produced by the uvula and soft palate at the back of the throat acting like a reed within the collapsible airway at this level. If that soft palate were not there, snoring would not occur; and if the airway at that level was large enough then there would likewise be no snoring. Treatments are therefore directed to one or both of these aspects. Surgical approaches to reducing the size of the palate have been borrowed from the veterinary world. Here English bulldogs, known to snore and indeed known to have a shortened life expectancy due to problems breathing during sleep, have an operation called uvulopalatopharyngoplasty or UPPP. This is effective at abolishing snoring, but may not be adequate treatment of any accompanying collapse of the breathing passage that would be associated with the phenomenon of sleep apnoea. The other treatments aimed at increasing the size of that breathing passage relate first of all to the nose. If it is difficult to breathe through the nose for any reason then a collapsing pressure is developed within the . upper airway. One can test this simply oneself by narrowing the nostrils a little with one's fingers and then breathing in. The negative pressure that is developed is obvious in one's ears and this applies to the airway in the back of the throat as well, so that treatment of any nasal stuffiness or nasal abnormality maybe very relevant. This is perhaps why smoking has such a relationship to snoring, since smokers tend to have a stuffy nose. The direct approach to increasing the size of that breathing tube is through one of two devices: one, a dental device which brings the lower jaw forward and with it the tongue so that the upper airway dimensions are increased; the other, a pump which blows air in through the nose in order to distend the airway and splint the breathing passage during sleep. This system goes by the name of nasal continuous positive airway pressure and is the mainstay of treatment of sleep apnoea which may accompany snoring. Simpler interventions should not be forgotten. Being overweight is very much linked to the worsening of snoring and the development of sleep apnoea. The reason for this is that the size of the airway mentioned before is also dependent upon the presence of excess fat in the neck. Weight loss has been shown to be beneficial. Likewise, sleep position may have a relevance. When lying on one's back of course the tongue tends to fall back against the back of the throat so narrowing the breathing passage further, and sleeping on one's side may alleviate this.

Another commonly accepted phenomenon of life is that of *jet lag*. This is a term used to describe the syndrome which develops when people fly across time zones. Upon arriving in a new time zone, the traveller is likely to find his or her body clock still set to the old time zone and therefore the timing of sleepiness, alertness, vigour, hunger, micturition, etc. may make adaptations to the social patterns of the new time zone uncomfortable. Trouble with sleep and intervals of reduced alertness are the most typical symptoms. An understanding of the response to these two changes in environmental time would help with the understanding of the management of jet lag. The internal clock which we all possess and which drives our bodily routines such as temperature variations across the day, hormone secretion and growth spurts, has an intrinsic rhythm of approximately twenty five and a half hours. We are entrained to the twenty-four hour day by exposure to light and to a lesser extent some other "zeitgeibers" which define the environment such as meals and other social events. The non twenty-four hour nature of our internal clock was determined by experiments where in which volunteers were placed in caves without any information about the days above them (no exposure to light and no contact with other individuals) and in this situation the individuals' days were extended to the twenty-five and a half hours. Sleep onset is delayed by something like an hour or an hour and a half every day until eventually the person sleeps in the middle of the day. We are able to entrain ourselves to the twenty-four hour day without ill effect which indicates that our internal systems can be adjusted by at least an hour and a half a day. It is believed that we can, in fact, adjust to something like two hours either way. This means that when, as a result of travel across time zones, the length of our day is altered we may not be able to bring all the body functions with circadian variation into line. Such functions include hormone secretion, temperature and of course sleep. The biology of the internal clock described here goes some way to explain the differences most people experience between flying east and west. With westward flight the day is lengthened. Beginning as we do at a 25½ day, and being able to adjust the clock by some 2 hours allows us to 'live' a 27½ hour day. A flight from London to Los Angeles therefore, crossing eight time zones and adding eight hours to the day, can be accommodated in just 2 or so days. In contrast, the return flight, with an eight hour shortening of the day and only about half an hour leeway in the clock (1½ hours being taken up each day in moving from 25½ to 24 hours) may require several days "rehabilitation". Hence the saying of the frequent flyer – "East is least, West is best". Can an understanding of this biology also help us minimise jet lag? Since the internal clock is timed by light exposure it is logical to encourage shifting of the clock by exposure to bright light, either naturally on arrival at the destination or on the plane by way of a bright-light visor. It cannot be stressed enough that being 'out and about' on arrival is important to entraining all the circadian systems to the new environment, but also that artificial systems if bright enough, could be an alternative worth considering.

OTHER BOOKS FROM AMBERWOOD PUBLISHING ARE:

Aromatherapy – A Guide for Home Use by Christine Westwood. All you need to know about essential oils and using them. £1.99.

Aromatherapy – For Stress Management by Christine Westwood. Covering the use of essential oils for everyday stress-related problems. £2.99.

Aromatherapy – For Healthy Legs and Feet by Christine Westwood. A comprehensive guide to the use of essential oils for the treatment of legs and feet, including illustrated massage instructions. £2.99.

Aromatherapy – Simply For You by Marion Del Gaudio Mak. A clear, simple and comprehensive guide to Aromatherapy for beginners. £1.99.

Aromatherapy – A Nurses Guide by Ann Percival SRN. This book draws on the author's medical skills and experience as a qualified aromatherapist to provide the ultimate, safe, lay guide to the natural benefits of Aromatherapy. Including recipes and massage techniques for many medical conditions and a quick reference chart. £2.99.

Aromatherapy – A Nurses Guide for Women by Ann Percival SRN. Building on the success of her first 'Nurses Guide', this book concentrates on women's health for all ages. Including sections on PMT, menopause, infertility, cellulite. Everything a woman needs to know about healthcare using aromatherapy. £2.99.

Aroma Science – The Chemistry & Bioactivity of Essential Oils by Dr Maria Lis-Balchin. With a comprehensive list of the Oils and scientific analysis – a must for all with an interest in the science of Aromatherapy. Includes sections on methodology, the sense of smell and the history of Aromatherapy. £4.99.

Plant Medicine – A Guide for Home Use (New Edition) by Charlotte Mitchell MNIMH. A guide to home use giving an insight into the wonderful healing qualities of plants. £2.99.

Woman Medicine – Vitex Agnus Castus by Simon Mills MA, FNIMH. The wonderful story of the herb that has been used for centuries in the treatment of women's problems. £2.99.

Ancient Medicine – Ginkgo Biloba (New Edition) by Dr Desmond Corrigan BSc(Pharms), MA, Phd, FLS, FPSI. Improved memory, circulation and concentration are associated in this book with medicine from this fascinating tree. £2.99.

Indian Medicine – The Immune System by Dr Desmond Corrigan BSc(Pharms), MA, Phd, FLS, FPSI. An intriguing account of the history and science of the plant called Echinacea and its power to influence the immune system. £2.99.

Herbal First Aid by Andrew Chevallier BA, MNIMH. A beautifully clear reference book of natural remedies and general first aid in the home. £2.99.

Natural Taste – Herbal Teas, A Guide for Home Use by Andrew Chevallier BA, MNIMH. This charmingly illustrated book contains a comprehensive compendium of Herbal Teas gives information on how to make it, its benefits, history and folklore. £2.99.

Garlic– How Garlic Protects Your Heart by Prof E. Ernst MD, PhD. Used as a medicine for over 4500 years, this book examines the latest scientific evidence supporting Garlic's effect in reducing cardiovascular disease, the Western World's number one killer. £3.99.

Signs & Symptoms of Vitamin Deficiency by Dr Leonard Mervyn BSc, PhD, C.Chem, FRCS. A home guide for self diagnosis which explains and assesses Vitamin Therapy for the prevention of a wide variety of diseases and illnesses. £2.99.

Causes & Prevention of Vitamin Deficiency by Dr Leonard Mervyn BSc, PhD, C.Chem, FRCS. A home guide to the Vitamin content of foods and the depletion caused by cooking, storage and processing. It includes advice for those whose needs are increased due to lifestyle, illness etc. £2.99.

Eyecare Eyewear – For Better Vision by Mark Rossi Bsc, MBCO. A complete guide to eyecare and eyewear including an assessment of the types of spectacles and contact lenses available and the latest corrective surgical procedures. £3.99.

RECOMMENDED READING

Herbal Medicine for Sleep & Relaxation by Dr Desmond Corrigan BSc(Pharms), MA, PhD, FLS, FPSI. An expertly written guide to the natural sedatives as an alternative to orthodox drug therapies, drawing on the latest medical research, presented in an easy reference format. £2.99.